D1231801

The rainbow Love puts in the sky to tell His children not to fear.

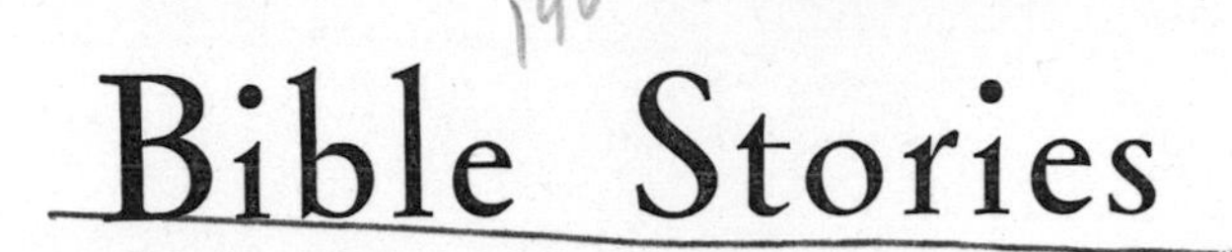

Bible Stories

AS TOLD TO
VERY LITTLE CHILDREN

BY Bessie Edmond Andruss

*

With Illustrations by
OLIVETTE

COWARD-McCANN, INC.
NEW YORK

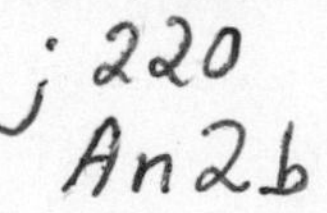

Ninth Impression

MANUFACTURED IN THE UNITED STATES
AT THE VAN REES PRESS

THIS BOOK IS LOVINGLY DEDICATED
TO THE MOTHERS OF THE WORLD

B. E. A.

Table of Contents

List of Illustrations in Color

Foreword

THESE STORIES are written with the object in view of making the Bible stories as interesting to very little children as the old-time fairy tales are to them.

In my many years' experience in telling Bible stories, I found that the small children grew restless and sleepy if historical facts were injected into the Bible stories.

I found, also, that the more spiritual the stories were, the better they understood them. It was very clear to these children that evil or error was really nothing in the presence of divine Love.

Thus, to tell them that divine Love destroyed evil, not men, was to present a consistent God to them, whom they could love and obey.

In telling these stories I have endeavored to impress upon the child thought what each Bible character stands for—Abraham for obedience, Moses for meekness, Joseph for forgiveness, and so on.

I have found it wiser not to shock the budding thought by telling any tragic episodes connected with the Bible stories.

BESSIE EDMOND ANDRUSS.

NOAH AND THE ARK

ONCE UPON A TIME, in the Bible days, there lived a man named Noah, and he had three sons, named Shem, Ham, and Japheth.

Now, God loved Noah very much, because Noah was always good and kind and loved everybody, and would do everything that God told him to do. Noah taught his three sons to love God too.

Now, all the other people at that time would not do what God told them to do, but instead they listened to error who told them to be naughty children, and not to listen to Love as Noah always did.

So Noah told them not to listen to error, but listen to God, for God was Love. But these people only laughed at good kind Noah, and poked fun at him.

One day God told Noah to build an Ark. Do you know what an Ark is? Well, it is a large flat boat, which looks like a house and floats on the water. God told Noah to put only one window in the Ark and only one door.

When Noah finished building the Ark, God came to him and told him to go into the Ark, with his wife and all his family, and take with him two little lambs and two camels, and two goats and two little kids, and two cows, and two little calves and two ravens. Do you know what a raven is? A raven is a bird that has all black feathers. And he also took two doves. Do you know what a dove is? A dove is a bird that has all white feathers.

There were a whole lot more birds and animals, little ones and big ones, which went into the Ark with Noah and his sons. Can you name any more that you think went in with Noah?

Well, after they all got in, God shut the door of the Ark tight, for he wanted to save Noah and his family and all those lovely animals and birds from getting wet, because there was going to be a great big rain, which would rain and rain and rain, until it would be a big flood of rain over everything.

That is the way error works. If you listen to error, it gets bigger and bigger, until it gets so big it just bursts!

So when God shut the door of the Ark, with Noah and his family inside with the animals, then error began at once to pour down the rain. My! how it did rain—and RAIN! It rained so hard that it soon covered up all the houses and trees, as well as all the big high hills and mountains.

But Noah and his wife and his three sons, Shem, Ham and Japheth, were not afraid of the rain, for they knew that Love was with them all the time, and had given them this beautiful Ark to keep them safe, and it could not rain on them. So the Ark just went sailing along on the water and they were all so happy because they were all good children.

One day after they had been sailing in the Ark for lots of days, Noah thought he would peep out of the window of the Ark and see if the water was just as deep as it had been. And when he peeped out, he saw that the water was not so deep as it had been, because the top of Mount Ararat had no water on it. Now, Mount Ararat is the name of the mountain where the Ark rested after it had been sailing around.

So Noah took one of the ravens, and opened the window of the Ark and put the raven out, and the raven flew away but came back in a little while and kept flying back and forth to the Ark.

Then Noah took one of the sweet, little, white doves, and put her out of the Ark window, but the little white dove would not stay out—because it was still too wet for her little feet—so she tapped on the Ark window for Noah to open the window and take her in again, which he did.

The next week he again put the little, white dove out the Ark window, and just when it was getting dark he heard a little tap at the window of the Ark, so he opened the window—and there was the little, white dove, with an olive leaf in her little mouth. So Noah took her into the Ark.

Then, Noah waited another week, and sent the little

white dove out again, and it was so nice and dry on the ground now that the little white dove flew away and did not come back to the Ark any more, but stayed in her home in the trees.

Then God told Noah to come out of the Ark, because all the ground was dry, and the trees and grass were all dry too. So Noah came out of the Ark, and so did all his family, and all the lovely animals and birds, and they all walked two by two out of the Ark as God had told them to do.

After they all left the Ark, Noah told his wife and his three sons, Shem, Ham, and Japheth, to look up at the sky. So they all looked, and there they saw a great, big, beautiful rainbow! Do you know what a rainbow is? Well, it is a big, half-round, beautiful thing full of lovely colors, which Love puts in the sky to tell His children not to fear, for He stops the rain with His beautiful rainbow.

Now, while Noah and his family were safe in God's Ark, error, which had made it rain so hard that it had become a flood, was destroyed.

So you see, error just punished itself as it always does, while God's perfect children were all happy and thanked Love for taking care of them as He always does.

Do you know in what book in the Bible you can read this story of Noah and the Ark? Well, I will tell you—the name of the book in the Bible is—Genesis.

OBEDIENT ABRAHAM

ONCE UPON A TIME, there lived in the Bible days a man named Abraham, who always obeyed God in everything that God told him to do. Abraham never asked God why did He want him to do this, or why did He want him to do that; but just as soon as God told Abraham what to do, Abraham did it at once.

Abraham had a wife named Sarah, but they did not have any little children. And God knew that they wanted a baby boy. So God told Abraham that He would give Abraham a baby boy, because Abraham had always been so obedient to Him. And God told Abraham and Sarah, his wife, to name the baby boy Isaac.

When God brought little Isaac to Abraham and Sarah, they just loved him so much that Abraham made a big feast for him. Do you know what a feast is? Well, it is a big party, where there is a whole lot of good things to eat.

Abraham loved little Isaac so much, that it looked like he loved little Isaac more than he loved God.

And we all know that we must love God the most of all, because God is Love and He gives us everything to make us happy.

So Love came to Abraham and talked with him to find

out if Abraham truly loved God more than he did little Isaac. And Love told Abraham to bring little Isaac to Him.

Now God did not really want Abraham to give up little Isaac, but Love just wanted to see if Abraham would truly give up little Isaac to God,—for Love only meant to show Abraham that God was the true Father of little Isaac and was taking care of little Isaac all the time.

Now, you remember that Abraham always obeyed God, whatever God told him to do. So, when Love told Abraham to give Him little Isaac,—just guess what Abraham said? Why, he said, yes, he would bring Isaac at once to God.

So, you see, Abraham really and truly did love God the most.

Now, in the Bible days, when the men wanted to show God that they loved Him, they would take some meat and put it on a table, called an altar. Then they would build a big fire under the altar, and roast this meat. But, they would not eat the meat, even though it would have tasted so good to them, because they wanted to show God that they could sacrifice for God. Do you know what a sacrifice means? It means to give up to someone else something you want yourself. Do you ever make sacrifices?

Now you and I know that roasting a piece of meat and giving it up for God, is not the way to show God that we love Him. But the way to show God that we really love Him is for us to be kind and loving to all of God's children, to sacrifice error for Love—to give up error for Love. But, you see, these people did not know any better when they roasted the meat, and sacrificed or gave it to God.

So, when God told Abraham to give up little Isaac and bring him to God, Abraham did not understand what God meant, for Abraham thought that God meant for him to put little Isaac on the altar, or table, just like the men did with the piece of meat.

Now wasn't that funny for Abraham to think that God meant such a thing? You and I know that God did not mean that at all.

For God is Love, and everything God does is loving and kind and good; and, as I told you before, God just meant to teach Abraham to love Him more than anyone else in the world.

So Abraham put little Isaac on the altar, but all the time Abraham had such faith in God as Love, that Abraham knew that God would take care of Isaac. That is why Abraham was not afraid to lay little Isaac on the altar with the sticks of wood under it.

And, the Bible doesn't say anything about little Isaac being afraid at all, so we know little Isaac was not afraid either, because he knew he was God's perfect child, and Love would not let anything hurt him.

Now, when Abraham placed little Isaac on the altar, and put the sticks of wood under the altar and was ready to light them—guess what happened!

Why, God sent the loveliest angel to Abraham, who took hold of Abraham's hand and told him not to light the fire.

And this lovely angel told Abraham that God loved

Abraham, and God was now sure that Abraham truly loved God the most of all.

And Abraham lifted little Isaac down from the altar, and took him home to his mama, Sarah, and they were all so happy.

And Abraham remained always obedient to God.

Do you know where you can find this story in the Bible? In the book called Genesis.

JACOB AND ESAU

WHEN LITTLE ISAAC grew up to be a big man, he married a beautiful lady named Rebekah.

And Isaac and Rebekah had two little boys, named Esau and Jacob.

Now error kept whispering into Isaac's ear to love Esau better than Jacob. Wasn't that naughty for Isaac to listen to error?

And Isaac did listen some more to that whisper, which told him to tell Esau that he would give him a birthright. Do you know what a birthright means? It means that all the riches which belong to a father and a mother will be given to the oldest child, and the other children will not get any of the riches.

But God does not do that way with His children, because God is Love. And Love gives to all His children just the same whether they are older or younger.

So Isaac petted and loved Esau, and told him that he would give him the birthright.

Rebekah knew that error was using Isaac, and making him give so much to Esau and not enough to Jacob, so she just loved Jacob all the more.

Jacob loved his mama too, and he was always obedient

to her. And as Jacob grew up he took care of all the sheep and all the little lambs which belonged to his father. He would feed them and give them water to drink, and he loved them.

Now Isaac and Rebekah and Esau and Jacob all lived in a tent for their home. And Jacob would stay in the tent with his mother, when he was not looking after the sheep and the little lambs, while Esau would go away into the fields and woods and stay all day.

One day Jacob cooked some delicious food, called pottage, for himself after he had finished his work. And he was just getting ready to enjoy it when Esau came in from the fields where he had been all day long by himself, without any food. My! but Esau was so very hungry; error was just telling him that he could not go another step until he got something to eat.

Now, just wasn't that foolish of Esau to stay so long away from his home—not to come home to lunch even—until he was so hungry he did not know what to do? You see how much wiser Jacob was, for Jacob cooked something for himself so he would not have to go hungry.

When Esau smelled that delicious pottage, which Jacob had cooked for himself, he got hungrier and hungrier. And Esau asked Jacob to give the pottage to him.

Now error was making Esau selfish. Esau knew that Jacob had made the pottage for himself, yet Esau wanted Jacob to give it to him.

Now you know, if Esau had listened to Love he would have asked his father to let him share his birthright with his younger brother Jacob. But Esau did not; he thought he wanted all the birthright for himself. And now when Esau was hungry, he wanted all the delicious pottage which Jacob had cooked for himself.

Jacob said, all right, he would give Esau the pottage, if Esau would give him the birthright.

Esau was so hungry he did not stop to think, but said, yes, Jacob could have his birthright, if Jacob would give him the pottage.

So Jacob gave the pottage to Esau. And, my! how Esau did eat! He ate, and ate, and Jacob gave him more and more, until it was all gone.

And Jacob did not have any pottage left for himself, but he did not care, because, you see, Esau had given Jacob the birthright.

Jacob knew that Esau did not love his birthright enough, or else he would not have given it to Jacob for the pottage—no matter how good the pottage tasted.

Now you and I know that if Isaac had given the birthright to Jacob, Jacob would have been too wise to sell it for a bowl of pottage.

So Jacob took Esau's birthright, and took good care of it.

You can find this story about Esau selling his birthright to Jacob in the book called Genesis in the Bible.

ESAU FORGIVES JACOB

Now, after Esau had eaten Jacob's delicious pottage and he was no longer hungry, error tempted Esau and Esau got angry with his brother Jacob, because Jacob took the birthright when Esau gave it to him.

Then Jacob went far away and married a beautiful lady named Rachel. And they lived there a long time and grew rich.

One day God told Jacob to take Rachel and their children, and the sheep and the little lambs, and go back to the country where Jacob used to live with his mother Rebekah and his father Isaac and his brother Esau.

So Jacob put Rachel and the children on the backs of the camels, and he got on a camel himself, and they all started off to go to the country where Jacob used to live when he was a little boy.

Do you know what a camel is? It is an animal with long legs, a long neck, and a big hump on its back.

Now Jacob remembered that his brother Esau let error make him angry with Jacob because Jacob took Esau's birthright in exchange for the pottage which Jacob cooked and Esau ate. And the same old error tried to make

Jacob afraid to go back to the country where Esau and Jacob used to live.

Error kept whispering to Jacob that Esau would not be kind to Jacob if he saw him; and that Jacob was afraid of his brother Esau.

So, one night while Rachel and the children and all the sheep and little lambs were resting beside a lovely brook, Jacob went off by himself so he could get rid of that wrong thought that he was afraid of his brother Esau.

You and I know that we must not be afraid of our brother, but we must love our brother, and we must know that our brother loves us.

While Jacob was alone, error tried its best to make Jacob believe that he was afraid of Esau. Error said Esau might hurt Jacob, and error said Esau did not love Jacob because Jacob took Esau's birthright. You never heard such a lot of foolishness as that old error tried to talk to Jacob.

But Jacob would not let error talk. Jacob just wrestled all night with that old error. Do you know what wrestling means? It means to try to throw down.

Jacob asked God to help him throw that old error down, and God sent His angel to take away the strength from error, and it became—nothing. And Jacob was so happy, because he was not afraid any more!

Jacob saw Truth and Love all around him, and saw that there wasn't any such thing as error at all. Jacob found out that error is nothing but a shadow, and when the Light of Truth comes in, error disappears.

When morning came Jacob was so happy, because he

had found out that Love was everywhere and error was nowhere.

Love told Jacob that because Jacob had been such a brave prince, and because Jacob was not afraid of error, Love would give him a new name, the name of Israel, which means a Prince of God; and God gave him power and strength to take care of himself.

Jacob called the place where he wrestled with error, and where he saw God as Love and always with him,—Peniel. Can you say this word, Peniel?

Now Jacob started off again on his journey to his old home, for he was not afraid any more to meet his brother Esau. For Jacob knew that God was taking care of him, and of Rachel, and his children, and of all the sheep and the little lambs.

So Jacob sent messengers out to find where Esau was, and the messengers came back and told Jacob that Esau was on his way to meet Jacob.

Then Jacob looked and saw his brother Esau coming. And guess what Esau did? Why, he ran up to his dear brother Jacob, and put his arms around him!

And they kissed each other, and loved each other, and were so glad to be together again.

Love had made Esau forgive his brother Jacob, and Love told Jacob to give his brother Esau a lot of presents to show Esau that he loved him. So Jacob gave Esau a lot of sheep and camels as presents, and Esau took them.

And they were all so happy together.

You will find this story in the book called Genesis, in the Bible.

THE LITTLE BOY JOSEPH

Now Jacob had twelve little boys, and the name of one of those boys was Joseph.

Joseph was a good boy. But the other boys, who were older than Joseph, did not behave so well.

And because Joseph obeyed his daddy all the time, his daddy gave Joseph a beautiful coat of many colors.

When Joseph's brothers saw Joseph wearing this beautiful coat, they wanted coats like it, but Jacob would not give them lovely coats like Joseph's, because they listened to error so much.

One day his daddy told Joseph to go and find his big brothers, who had gone far away from their home to feed the sheep in the fields.

When Joseph's big brothers saw Joseph coming toward them, error told those big brothers to take Joseph's beautiful coat of many colors away from him and tear it all up.

Now one brother's name was Reuben, and he did not listen to error as much as the other big brothers did. So Reuben told his brothers not to hurt Joseph, but to throw Joseph down into a big pit, and leave him there all by himself.

If Reuben had not listened to error at all, he would not

have told them to throw Joseph into the pit either, but he would have taken care of his brother.

Do you know what a pit is? A pit is a big, deep, deep hole in the ground.

So, after Joseph's brothers took Joseph's beautiful coat of many colors away from Joseph, the error in their thought made these big brothers throw Joseph down, down into the deep, deep pit.

Now, what do you think Joseph did when he found himself down in this deep, deep pit?

Joseph knew that God is Love, and he knew that Love was right down there with him in the deep, deep pit, and he knew also that Love would lift him up out of the pit.

So Joseph was not afraid because he had always been a good, obedient little boy, and Joseph knew that God was his true Father-Mother-God, and loved him, and He was taking care of him and would let nothing hurt him.

After they had thrown Joseph into the pit, these naughty brothers were sitting down eating some lunch when they saw some men coming riding on camels.

One brother, named Judah, said, Let us sell Joseph to these men. So Reuben went to the pit to take Joseph out to sell him to the men who came riding on the camels. Reuben looked in the pit, but Joseph was not there!

My, but those naughty brothers were scared! That is just what happens to every one who listens to error. It makes him afraid.

But if everybody would only listen to God, divine Love, all the time, he would never, never be afraid!

Now just guess what had happened to Joseph, so that his naughty brothers could not find him.

Well, I will tell you. You see, Joseph was not afraid because he just knew that Love would take him out of the deep pit—and, sure enough, Love made some people come along and lift Joseph out of the pit.

And these people put Joseph on one of their camels, and they all went riding into a big country called Egypt.

There they sold Joseph to a man named Potiphar, who was the captain of King Pharaoh's soldiers.

Now, while Joseph was riding to Egypt, his big brothers had to go back home to their father, and they did not know what to tell him about Joseph.

So error told these brothers to say that an animal had eaten up Joseph; and they made believe the animal had torn up Joseph's pretty coat. Wasn't that naughty of these brothers to tell such a story to their father?

Of course Jacob cried for his little boy Joseph. But Love was everywhere, taking care of both Jacob and Joseph, and Love was unfolding the way to bring Jacob and his darling little boy Joseph together again, so they could live together in happiness and in great joy.

I will tell you about this in the next story, and when you hear what I will tell you it will make you so glad that Joseph was taken to Egypt.

You will find this story about the little boy Joseph in the book called Genesis, in the Bible.

JOSEPH A BIG MAN

After Joseph went to live in Egypt with King Pharaoh's Captain Potiphar, and Joseph grew up to be a big man, error told stories about Joseph to Captain Potiphar, and because he believed these stories, Captain Potiphar locked Joseph up in a prison.

Do you think Joseph was afraid when he was locked in prison? Oh, my! No, indeed! Joseph knew Love was everywhere, he knew Love was in the prison with him and some day Love would take him out of the old prison and give him riches and friends—just the same way Love took him out of the deep pit and brought him into Egypt.

While Joseph was in the prison he was learning more about Love all the time. He learned that Love makes us wise and shows us how to take care of all the good which Love gives us, if we will only look to Love to give us all we need.

So Joseph knew that Love was teaching him how to be wise, and he knew when he was wise enough Love would unlock the prison door and take him out.

And, sure enough, Love told King Pharaoh to take Joseph out of the prison, and Love told King Pharaoh to listen to all Joseph said to him, for Love had taught Joseph how to be wise.

So King Pharaoh told the keeper of the prison to unlock the door and bring Joseph to him, and Joseph knew it was Love who had told King Pharaoh to unlock the prison door and let him out.

So Joseph told King Pharaoh all the wise things that Love had taught him while he was in prison, because Joseph had been so close to Love there and he learned that Love knew everything.

Joseph told King Pharaoh that in seven years' time, error was going to talk to the people and scare them so much that the people would believe the ground would not grow any more food for them to eat, and everybody would have to go hungry, unless King Pharaoh would commence right away to put away carefully all the food which the people did not need. Because Love had just filled their land with bushels and bushels and bushels of food, and they had so much food they could not eat it all.

Joseph also told King Pharaoh that if King Pharaoh would take care of all this food and keep it for seven years, until the time came when error would make the people believe they did not have any food—then King Pharaoh could sell the food to the people and make them happy by feeding them all they wanted to eat. And, also, selling the food to the people would make King Pharaoh rich.

Well, King Pharaoh was so delighted with Joseph for telling him these wise things, that King Pharaoh put a beautiful gold ring on Joseph's finger and dressed him up in beautiful clothes, and gave Joseph a lot of money and a beautiful house to live in.

Now Joseph knew that King Pharaoh gave him all these good things because Love had told King Pharaoh to do so. For Joseph had been obedient to Love and had learned all the lessons which Love had given him to learn.

Then King Pharaoh made Joseph a governor, and everybody had to ask Joseph for everything. And, because Joseph knew the truth about Love giving plenty of food all the time, and because Joseph knew that error was nothing at all—the people looked to him and loved him.

And Joseph was happy because Love had brought him safely into Egypt, so he could feed everybody, when error told the people they did not have any more food.

Now, you remember, Joseph's big brothers had listened to error when it told them to throw Joseph into the deep pit and to tear up Joseph's beautiful coat of many colors. Well, when these big brothers grew up to be men, they still listened to error just the same, and when error told them the ground would not grow any more food for them to eat, they were afraid they would go hungry.

So their father told Joseph's big brothers to go down to Egypt to buy some food, because he had heard that a big man, the governor, had lots of food to sell. But Jacob did not know this big man, the governor, was his own darling boy Joseph, because, you remember, Joseph's big brothers believed Joseph was lost when he was a little boy after the big brothers had thrown him into the deep pit. And Jacob believed an animal had eaten Joseph, for error had made these naughty brothers tell their father this untrue story.

So Joseph's brothers came down to Egypt to buy food, and, of course, they had to go to Joseph to ask him to sell them some food.

And when these big brothers asked Joseph to please sell them some food, they did not know this big man, the governor, was Joseph.

But Joseph knew these men were his brothers, and if Joseph had listened to error, he would have said, No, I will not sell you this food because you hurt me and threw me into that dark, deep pit. Do you think Joseph listened to that error?

You and I know Joseph only listened to Love, and Joseph was so loving to his brothers that he not only sold them all the food they wanted, but he gave them back all their money too.

Still, Joseph wanted to teach these naughty brothers a lesson and make them sorry they had listened to error and been so naughty.

So Joseph locked up one brother, named Simeon, and Joseph told the other brothers to go home and that he would keep Simeon with him until the other brothers came back to buy some more food, and also the next time they came they must bring their little brother whose name was Benjamin.

Now, whenever people let error make them naughty, and then they find out their naughtiness is known, they always get scared.

But, if we are always loving and kind, like Joseph always was, nothing can make us afraid.

So, when Joseph's big brothers found out Joseph was not going to let the brother, named Simeon, go back home with them, and that Simeon was locked up, they got scared and told each other this big man, the governor, was keeping Simeon and making them bring back their little brother Benjamin, because they had been naughty and listened to error and thrown their own brother Joseph into the deep pit.

Oh, my! how sorry these big brothers became right then and there. How they wished they had listened to Love, as their brother Joseph had always done; and how they wished they had not listened to that error, but had made error nothing at all!

Now that is just what Joseph wanted to happen. That is why he locked up Simeon and sent for the little brother Benjamin. And when Joseph saw how sorry his big brothers were that they had listened to error and been so unkind to Joseph, Joseph's eyes filled with tears of gladness, and he turned his back to his brothers and cried with joy. For Joseph knew that just as soon as his brothers were sorry for their naughtiness, they would stop listening to error and listen to Love.

So Joseph let his brothers go home, and told them to be sure to bring little Benjamin next time they came, and then he would give back Simeon to them.

Very soon the big brothers and their father had no more food, so again the big brothers had to go down to Egypt to buy some food from the governor. And the brothers told their father they would have to take Benjamin with them, because the governor said they must bring him. So Jacob said they could take Benjamin with them, but the big brothers must take good care of him.

Now when Joseph knew his big brothers and his young brother Benjamin were coming to see him to buy some more food, Joseph had his servant cook a whole lot of good things to eat to make a big party to give his brothers when they got to Egypt.

And when Joseph's brothers got to Egypt, and Joseph took them into the dining room, they saw the lovely party which Joseph had ready for them and they were so happy. And Joseph gave little Benjamin more goodies than he did the big brothers, because you see little brother Benjamin had not been naughty like the big brothers.

Then Joseph sold his big brothers all the food they needed to take back to their father. And Joseph told his servants to put the big brothers' money back into the bags with the food, and Joseph also told the servants to put a beautiful silver cup which belonged to Joseph in little Benjamin's bag.

Now Joseph was going to play a little trick on his big brothers by putting the silver cup in little Benjamin's bag. He was going to make believe he thought the big brothers had taken the silver cup when nobody was looking and had put it into little Benjamin's bag to take home with them.

Why do you suppose Joseph was going to play this trick on his big brothers? Because Joseph wanted to teach his big brothers a lesson by showing them that if Joseph wanted to listen to error he could say the big brothers had taken his silver cup and he could have them put in prison and locked up.

So when the servants of Joseph came up to the big brothers, who were on their way home, and made believe they knew the big brothers had taken Joseph's beautiful silver cup, the big brothers said they had not taken the cup and it was not in their bags. But the servants said they must open all the bags to see whether the beautiful silver cup was in their bags or not.

When all the bags had been opened, except little Benjamin's bag, the servants said they must open little Benjamin's bag too. The big brothers kept saying the cup was not in little Benjamin's bag. But the servants opened little Benjamin's bag, and, oh! those big brothers were so surprised to see the silver cup there.

Then fear came to these big brothers that now this big man, the governor, who had been so kind to them and given them the lovely party, would think they had taken the beautiful silver cup themselves and put it in little Benjamin's bag, and so he would lock them up in prison.

But you and I know that the governor was good, kind Joseph, and that Joseph was only playing a trick on them.

When the servant of Joseph found the beautiful silver cup in Benjamin's bag, Joseph told his big brothers that they must give Benjamin to him and the brothers could go back to their father. (Joseph, you know, was only making believe all the time.)

Then his brother Judah told Joseph that their father would feel very sad if they left little Benjamin in Egypt, because at one time their father had a little boy named Joseph, and he lost this darling little boy. (Judah did not know that he was talking to this same little Joseph, grown up to be a big man.) And now, if they went back to their father without little Benjamin, Jacob would cry some more over losing little Benjamin too.

Then Joseph told everybody to go out of the room but his brothers, and Joseph told his brothers that he was their own dear brother Joseph who had grown into a big man.

And Joseph kissed his brothers and put his arms around them. And Joseph told his brothers not to be afraid of him for he would not hurt them because he loved them.

Joseph also told his brothers not to feel sorry for him because they had listened to error and had thrown Joseph into the pit.

Joseph said if they had not thrown him into the pit, the men could not have sold him to King Pharaoh, and he never would have been made the governor.

And Joseph told his brothers how Love took care of him and how grateful he was to Love for this care, and also that Love was letting him feed so many people so they need not go hungry.

So Joseph sent for his dear father Jacob, whom he loved so much. My, but Jacob did hug and kiss his boy Joseph, and thanked God for giving Joseph back to him again.

Joseph gave his father a beautiful home and fine clothes, and lots of money, and also gave all these good things to his brothers as well. And they all lived together happily.

And all this happiness came about because Joseph let Love teach him to be wise and good.

Do you know where you can read this story about Joseph when he grew up to be a big man? In the book called Genesis in the Bible.

MOSES AND THE PRINCESS

ONCE UPON A TIME, in the Bible days, there were a whole lot of people called the Children of Israel; and they were God's perfect children for they loved God, and they knew that He was their loving Father-Mother-God.

Now there lived in the same place with these Children of Israel, a king, named Pharaoh; and this king let error talk to him, so he became very naughty.

And error told this naughty king not to let the Children of Israel have any little baby boys. So this naughty king told the Children of Israel that they could have little baby girls, all they wanted, but they could not have any little baby boys at all!

Now one day, the princess, who was the daughter of Pharaoh, the naughty king, went down to a river called the Nile to take a bath.

Did you ever go bathing in a big river, or ocean? Well, that is what the princess was doing, bathing in this long river. She took her maid with her.

In the River Nile were growing some flowers, called flags. While the princess was looking at the flags, she saw a pretty basket made of bulrushes, floating in the river among the flags. She called her maid to bring the basket to her. And, when the princess looked inside the basket, guess what she saw there! Why, it was a little, tiny, baby boy!

Just think of it—a little baby, in a pretty basket made of bulrushes, floating along the river, without a mama! Now how do you suppose this baby got there? Well, I will tell you how he got there.

You see, when this little baby boy was given to his mama, she knew that the naughty king would listen to error, and would not let her keep him; so she thought, if the princess found the baby boy, she would love him so much that her father, the naughty king, would let her keep the little baby boy.

So that is why the mama put her little baby in the basket, so the princess could find him.

When the princess asked her father, the naughty king, if she could keep the lovely little baby, the king said, Yes, you may keep him for your very own. That time the king listened to Love, and not to error.

The princess was so happy, for she loved the little baby boy, and she named him Moses.

Now, the princess needed a nurse to take care of the baby, and a little maid, who was really the baby Moses' own sister, told the princess she knew where to find one. The princess did not know the little maid was Moses' sister, so she told her to get the nurse, and the maid got the baby's very own mama—who was also the maid's mama, you remember—and brought her to the princess. Then, the princess told the mama, she must take care of little Moses.

Oh, but this mama was so happy, to take care of her own little baby again, and feed him and love him. And the little Moses was so happy, living with the princess and his mama.

Do you know in what book in the Bible you can read this story about Moses? You may read it in the book called Exodus.

MOSES AND THE CHILDREN OF ISRAEL

When the little baby Moses grew up to be a big man, like our daddies, he saw that wrong thoughts were coming to King Pharaoh again, and telling him to make the Children of Israel work hard all the time and not to let them play at all. Never, never could they play. And Moses also saw that King Pharaoh would bow down and worship idols made from wood and brass, instead of bowing down to God and loving God with his whole heart, as Moses did.

Now you remember that Moses really belonged to the Children of Israel, even though King Pharaoh had given Moses to his daughter, the princess, when she found him in the bulrushes in a basket when he was a tiny, little baby.

Moses was such a loving, kind, and meek man, that he knew it was not right for the Children of Israel to work so hard and not have any play time. Moses knew that God is a loving Father, and that He gives His children lots of time to play, as well as work, and lots and lots of time to be happy, always.

So Moses told the Children of Israel to leave this error, and to follow Love, and Love would lead them to a beautiful land where they could be happy—a land that was full of delicious fruits, and all kinds of good things to eat; and running brooks of water, and rivers to go bathing in where they could have a lovely time. Oh! yes, and lots of beautiful flowers and trees.

Then the Children of Israel let Moses lead them away from this error that was whispering to King Pharaoh; and they walked all the long way to get to this beautiful land which Moses told them Love promised to give them if they would be obedient children and leave error and follow Love.

Now when this naughty King Pharaoh saw that good, kind, and meek Moses had led the Children of Israel away from him and they were on their way to the beautiful land that Love had promised to give them, he called all his men (and these men were called Egyptians), and told them to hitch their fast horses, big black ones and big white ones, to chariots, and drive fast after the Children of Israel and bring them back, so he could make them do more hard work for him. Do you know what a chariot is? A chariot is a small carriage, without any seat in it, and you have to stand up in it to drive the horses.

When Moses saw these bad Egyptians coming after the Children of Israel he told the Children of Israel not to be afraid, for Love would take care of them, and Love would not let these Egyptians catch up to them, nor take them back to error.

So the Children of Israel kept marching on to get to this beautiful land that Love was going to give to them. Moses kept telling them more about Love all the time, telling them to be good children, and love Love with all their hearts.

Just guess what Love did for these dear Children of Israel! Why, Love made a great big pillar of fire at night for a light to show them the best pathway to march in. Oh, my! how bright this light made their path! Just as light as day! But error kept the Egyptians in the dark all the time, so they did not see this great big light which Love had given to His children.

At last, after the Children of Israel had marched for some time they had to stop their marching because there in front of them was a big sea. Do you know what a sea is? It is like the ocean where your daddy and your mama take you to wade and dig in the sand. Well, this big sea the Children of Israel saw before them is called the Red Sea.

When the Children of Israel got to this Red Sea, they did not know what to do, for the bad, old Egyptians were back of them and the big Red Sea was in front of them. Then Moses told the Children of Israel not to be afraid for Love would take care of them, and Love would never let the Egyptians catch them. Moses also told them to stand still and watch what Love would do to save them.

Then Moses, with a rod—a long stick of wood—which he had in his hand, stretched out his arm over the Red Sea. And, just guess what happened!

Why, Love made this big Red Sea part right down the middle and roll back on both sides. And the Children of Israel when they saw this dry ground like a path, were so happy. And they marched right over to the other side, to the dry land—thanking Love all the time for taking care of them all the way.

Now, when the Egyptians saw the Children of Israel marching through the sea, they thought they could go across through the sea, too, but Love never helps error; so Moses, taking his rod again in his hand, stretched his arm out over the Red Sea—and whack! bang! the water came rolling together and covered up the dry path, and instead there was a big ocean again.

So the Egyptians could not get over to the other side where the Children of Israel were nice and dry on the land, with Love taking care of them.

Now, you see, Love just took away all power from that error that was talking to the Egyptians, and made error nothing at all!

Then Moses and the Children of Israel sang together and loved God all the more for His goodness to them.

Now, although the Children of Israel had gotten across the Red Sea on their way to the beautiful country which God was going to give them, yet they still had a long way to go to get there. They had to go through the wilderness, —a wilderness is a place where there are no houses and no stores, no place to buy any food to eat at all.

The Children of Israel got very hungry and they could not get anything to eat because they were in this wilderness. But Moses knew where he could get some food for them; he knew that all he had to do was to ask Love for food, and Love would give it to them. So Moses told the Children of Israel not to fear, and he would ask Love to feed them.

And Moses asked Love to give them food—and guess what Love did? Why, He just rained down the most delicious cakes you ever ate, called manna; and the Children of Israel ate and ate and ate them, until they could not eat any more—for they had all they wanted. You see Love always does give us all we need when we ask Him.

The next time the Children of Israel got hungry they asked God to give them meat to eat, instead of more of the manna, because you see they had eaten so much of these delicious cakes they were tired of them. So this time God rained down quail for them to eat. Do you know what a quail is? It is quite a large bird, and tastes something like chicken when you eat it.

Then the Children of Israel wanted some water to drink. Now there was no water in the wilderness at all. But Moses knew that Love would give them water, and sure enough, Love showed Moses a big rock and told Moses to strike it with his rod, which Moses always carried in his hand.

So Moses struck the rock with the rod, then, bubbling out of the rock, came a whole lot of lovely fresh water. My! how those Children of Israel did drink, for they had all they wanted to drink.

Do you see how Love gives us, all the time, everything to make us happy?

Do you know where you can find this story about Moses and the Children of Israel in the Bible? You may find it in the book called Exodus.

MOSES AND THE TEN COMMANDMENTS

ONE DAY GOD CALLED MOSES to come up to the top of a mountain, named Mount Sinai, and God told Moses to put his brother Aaron in charge of the Children of Israel while Moses was up on the mountain talking to God.

When Moses reached the top of Mount Sinai, Moses found it was very still and quiet and peaceful up there. You see it is always quiet and still and peaceful wherever God comes to talk to us, and our thoughts have to be just full of love for everybody to hear God's voice when he speaks.

And Moses loved the Children of Israel so much, and he wanted to help them to be good children. That is why God called Moses to Mount Sinai, because God knew Moses loved the Children of Israel better than Moses loved himself.

So, when God spoke to Moses up there on that still, quiet, and peaceful mountain, He told Moses He had brought him two great big stones, and He wanted Moses to write on the stones all the Commandments God would tell Moses to write.

Now, why do you suppose God told Moses to write the Commandments on stones? You see, if the Commandments had been written on a piece of paper, or on a piece of wood, the Commandments would not have lasted forever, and God wanted these Commandments to last forever. And so they will, because they are written on stone, and that means the Commandments are written on such a strong foundation that nothing can ever destroy them.

And this strong foundation means that the Commandments are really written in the heart and mind of every one of God's children, because God has written them there just as Moses wrote them on the stones.

And when all of God's children set to work to learn the Commandments, they find out these Commandments are written in Mind, and Love unfolds them to us each day, until we know them all by heart.

The hand of God wrote the Commandments.

Now after Moses had finished writing the Commandments, Moses had to learn the meanings of the Commandments so he could tell the Children of Israel when he came down from the quiet and peaceful mountain.

Of course Moses could not teach the Children of Israel everything at once that these wonderful Commandments mean, because each Commandment has so many meanings that it takes a long time to find out all the true meanings of each Commandment.

Let us learn just one meaning of each Commandment, which Moses wrote on the stones, and then we shall be taking our first footsteps, and later on we shall learn more and more meanings—which will be taking more and more footsteps.

First of all, just guess how many Commandments God told Moses to write on the stones.

God told Moses to write just Ten Commandments on the stones. Now let me tell you some of the meanings which have been found in studying these commandments, and you may hunt for some other meanings yourself—for everybody hunts for different meanings in these wonderful Commandments.

This is the First Commandment:

Thou shalt have no other gods before me.

Some of the meanings of this commandment are that you must love God the most of all; that you must love to be good, *first* of all; that you must never love to be naughty, only love to be good.

And, also, you must love to be good, even more than you love candy, or pretty clothes, or dolls, or balls, or anything.

And, when you love to be good, first of all, God will then give you everything to make you happy.

This is the Second Commandment:

> *Thou shalt not make unto thee any graven image, or any likeness of anything that is in heaven above, or that is in the earth beneath or that is in the water under the earth: thou shalt not bow down thyself to them, nor serve them: for I the Lord thy God am a jealous God, visiting the iniquity of the fathers upon the children unto the third and fourth generation of them that hate me; and shewing mercy unto thousands of them that love me, and keep my commandments.*

Now this graven image, which God says we must not make, means a picture which error would make in our thought and call it just as real and good as divine Love, but it is not good at all, and only harms us—making believe to us that it is the likeness of Good, and asking us to bow down and serve it the way we should serve God.

Can you mention some of the graven images which error would try and make us bow down to and serve? I can name some. One is that old self, which wants everything for itself, and another false god, or graven image, is fear; and still another false god, which error tries to make us bow down to, is the belief that we can be sick.

We must never, never bow down to this false god, or graven image, because we know the truth that divine Love makes His children well and never makes them sick.

Now the other part of this big Second Commandment says,

I the Lord thy God am a jealous God.

This means that divine Love is guarding and watching His children, to see that error does not talk to them to try to turn their thoughts away from Love and to try to make God's perfect children love error instead of loving Good all the time.

So you see, "I the Lord thy God am a jealous God," really means I the Lord thy God am a watchful God.

"Visiting the iniquity," means that error keeps punishing itself until it becomes nothing at all, while God keeps pouring out more love and goodness on His perfect children, because they keep His Commandments.

This is the Third Commandment:

> *Thou shalt not take the name of the Lord thy God in vain; for the Lord will not hold him guiltless that taketh his name in vain.*

Now when you ask God to heal you or to give you what you need, you must believe God will do so, or else you are taking His name in vain. And whenever we are tempted to speak in a naughty way about God, or say naughty words, or speak in anger, that is also taking God's name in vain, for you know that God's name is Love. And if we are not loving we are taking Love's name in vain.

This is the Fourth Commandment, which is another big Commandment, like the Second Commandment:

> *Remember the sabbath day, to keep it holy.*
>
> *Six days shalt thou labour, and do all thy work:*
>
> *But the seventh day is the sabbath of the Lord thy God: in it thou shalt not do any work, thou, nor thy son, nor thy daughter, thy manservant, nor thy maid-servant, nor thy cattle, nor thy stranger that is within thy gates:*
>
> *For in six days the Lord made heaven and earth, the sea, and all that in them is, and rested the seventh day: wherefore the Lord blessed the sabbath day, and hallowed it.*

The sabbath means to rest from labor or work. Now we know that God has made everything that is good, and there is nothing else to be made, for everything is finished and perfect. And when everybody wakes up to know this he will see that God has finished all the good that there ever can be, and all we have to do is just to reflect God's finished work.

And, we must remember also, that we do not have to work to get well and strong. God has already made us well and strong, because all of God's work is finished. And all we have to do is to rest in the Truth and know that everything in the world is perfect and complete—then we will be keeping the sabbath day holy.

And we also keep the sabbath day holy by going to Sunday school and to church to learn how God completed his perfect work.

Now this is the Fifth Commandment:

> *Honour thy father and thy mother: that thy days may be long upon the land which the Lord thy God giveth thee.*

We know that the father and mother of everybody is God, divine Love, and we honour our Father-Mother-God by loving to be good, and by obeying our mamas and our daddies, and also by keeping well and happy.

Our Father-Mother-God has made us well and happy, and when we know that nothing can hurt or harm God's perfect child, we are honouring our Father-Mother-God.

Now, this is the Sixth Commandment. It is a very short commandment, for it has only four words in it, so we will call it a baby commandment. Because it is so short, a baby could learn it, and it will be so easy for you to remember. It is

Thou shalt not kill.

Now, we know that God's perfect child cannot be killed, because God is his life, and nobody could kill God. Then what does, "Thou shalt not kill" mean? We must not kill anyone's good thoughts or stop him from being good. If we see a little child who is good and loving and obedient, we must not try to kill that child's thoughts and make the child naughty, unloving and disobedient.

The next is the Seventh Commandment:

Thou shalt not commit adultery.

We must not mix error with Truth, nor mix the bad with the good. You would not pour sour milk with sweet milk, for that would make the sweet milk all bad, and you wouldn't drink it. Neither must we mix our good and pure thoughts with the bad, or naughty thoughts, for the bad and naughty thoughts would rob us of our pure and good thoughts.

We must keep our thoughts pure and good all the time, and we must not let error adulterate our thoughts in any way. Ad-ul-ter-ate is a big word, and means to mix the impure or bad with the good. See if you can say it.

This is the Eighth Commandment:

Thou shalt not steal.

Now we know that everything good we have has been given to us by divine Love, so of course Love will not let error steal anything from us.

And we must not allow error to steal our good thoughts from us, nor must we steal other children's good thoughts. We must be careful not to make other children angry, nor unhappy, for if we do we shall have stolen away their good thoughts of joy and happiness.

This is the Ninth Commandment:

Thou shalt not bear false witness against thy neighbor.

Do you know what a neighbor is? A neighbor is one who lives near by. Well, you live the nearest to yourself, so, of course, you are your own neighbor too, as well as someone else who lives near you.

To "bear false witness" means not to tell the truth or not to think the truth. When we say or think that we are sick or unhappy, we are bearing false witness, for it is not the truth.

The truth is that God has made us well and strong, and God has finished His work.

Then to think we are sick is bearing false witness against our true self, or our neighbor.

And, if we look at any one of God's other perfect children, and see error in that child we are also bearing false witness against our neighbor.

Now, this is the Tenth and last Commandment:

> *Thou shalt not covet thy neighbor's house,*
> *thou shalt not covet thy neighbor's wife,*
> *nor his manservant, nor his maidservant,*
> *nor his ox, nor his ass, nor anything that is*
> *thy neighbor's.*

To covet means to want what does not belong to you, but belongs to someone else.

Now, you see, God has given His children everything that is good. There is nothing that they cannot have that is good, if they just ask Love to give it to them.

And, if we look at what someone else has, and believe that he has something better than what God has given to us, and we want to take away from him what belongs to him—we are coveting what does not belong to us.

And the Tenth Commandment says, "Thou shalt not covet,"—so we must want only just what we know God gives to us.

Now we have finished all the Ten Commandments, which Moses wrote on the stones, and we have learned one meaning of each Commandment.

So, in the next story, we shall learn what Moses did when he finished writing the Commandments on the stones.

You will find the Ten Commandments in the twentieth chapter of the book called Exodus, in the Bible.

AARON AND THE GOLDEN CALF

When Moses had written all the Commandments, or God's laws, on the two big stones, and had learned them, he came down from the mountain, called Mount Sinai, to take these stones with the Commandments written on them to the Children of Israel.

My, but Moses was so happy to take all the wonderful laws of God to the Children of Israel, because Moses knew that if the Children of Israel obeyed these laws of God, they would always be well, happy and rich.

But, when Moses got to the Children of Israel, guess what he saw. Why, Moses saw a golden calf, and error was making the Children of Israel dance around the golden calf, and bow down to it, making a false god of it. While Moses was watching the Children of Israel bow down to the golden calf, which was a false god, error made Moses throw down the big stones with the Ten Commandments written on them, and break them all to pieces. You see error always does break the Ten Commandments.

Then Moses called his brother Aaron, and asked him where the golden calf had come from. So Aaron told Moses how error came to the Children of Israel, while

Moses was up on Mount Sinai with God, and how error made the Children of Israel bring all their gold rings and bracelets and earrings, and how error made Aaron build a big fire and throw all these gold rings and bracelets and earrings into the big fire,—and out came the golden calf.

So Moses took the golden calf and threw it into the fire, and it melted away. And Aaron was so sorry that he had listened to wrong thoughts, and let the Children of Israel bow down to the false god.

And Moses separated the Children of Israel from that error, and the Children of Israel went with Moses to serve divine Love, and they promised that they would not have any other god before divine Love.

God called Moses up to Mount Sinai again and gave him two more big stones. And God told Moses to write the Ten Commandments all over again and to take them to the Children of Israel.

So Moses wrote the Ten Commandments the second time, and brought them back to the Children of Israel.

This time error could not break the Commandments, because Love was with the Children of Israel. And when Love is with God's children, there is not any error anywhere to break the Commandments. And God's children love to obey the Commandments because it keeps them well, happy, and rich.

The story of Aaron and the golden calf is in the book called Exodus, in the Bible.

LITTLE SAMUEL

ONCE UPON A TIME, in the Bible days, there lived a lady, named Hannah.

Now, in the Bible days, they used to call a church, the Temple, or the Temple of the Lord.

And Hannah used to go up to the Temple and pray to God, and also to learn more about God from a man named Eli, who lived in the Temple and took care of it, and taught the people all about God.

Hannah did not have any little children at all, but she made a promise that if ever she had a little baby boy, she would take him to the Temple of the Lord, and let Eli teach him about divine Love, because she would want him to work for God and be His obedient child.

So one day, sure enough, a little baby boy was given to this lady, named Hannah, and she loved him very much.

Hannah named the baby boy Samuel.

When little Samuel got big enough to talk, his mama, Hannah, used to tell him all about Truth and Love.

Hannah taught little Samuel that Love was always with him, and that little Samuel was God's perfect child.

You remember that Hannah had made a promise that

if ever a little boy was given to her, she would give the baby to divine Love.

And, because his mama had taught little Samuel so much about Truth and Love, little Samuel knew that Truth and Love were with him all the time.

When little Samuel grew bigger, Hannah took him to the Temple of the Lord, to see Eli, the good man who lived in the Temple and taught the people how to serve God.

When Eli saw Samuel, he loved Samuel right away, and Eli knew Samuel was ready to serve Truth and Love, because Samuel's mama Hannah had taught him to love Truth and Love.

One day when Hannah and Samuel were in the Temple of the Lord, Eli asked Hannah to leave Samuel with him to stay all night in the Temple of the Lord.

Hannah said, yes, Samuel could stay with good, kind Eli, and so she went home and left little Samuel with Eli.

Of course, Samuel was delighted to stay in the lovely Temple of the Lord, for the Temple of the Lord was so quiet and still that little Samuel could think more about divine Love, and then he could help Eli in his work in the Temple of the Lord. And this made Samuel so proud, because he loved to serve God.

After little Samuel and Eli had said their prayers and sung praises to God, they went to bed. Eli gave Samuel a bed for himself, and Eli went to his own bed.

Just when little Samuel was getting ready to fall asleep, guess what happened! Why, he heard a voice calling: "Samuel."

Little Samuel sat up in bed and looked all around, but there wasn't anyone there. So he jumped out of his bed, and ran to Eli, saying: "Here am I." And little Samuel asked Eli why he had called him. But Eli was surprised to see Samuel standing by his bed, and Eli told Samuel he did not call him. Eli said, You go back to bed.

Little Samuel went back to bed, and suddenly he heard someone calling again: "Samuel."

Samuel jumped out of bed the second time, and went to Eli and said: "Here am I, you did call me." Eli said, No, I did not call you—just go back to bed.

So little Samuel went back to bed again, but he did not know what to think, because he knew someone had called him, and yet Eli kept saying he had not called him.

When Samuel got into his bed this time, and was just about to go to sleep, he heard someone calling him for the third time, saying: "Samuel."

When Samuel got out of his bed this time and went to Eli, he asked Eli if Eli did not really and truly call him, and Eli told him, no, he had not called him.

Then Eli told little Samuel it was divine Love calling him, that divine Love wanted to see if Samuel was ready to serve Him always.

And Eli told little Samuel that when he heard the voice of divine Love again he should answer and say: "Speak, Lord, for Thy servant heareth."

Little Samuel was filled with joy when Eli told him it was divine Love calling to him.

So Samuel went quietly back to bed, and he kept so still

in bed, waiting for the voice of divine Love to come to him again.

And sure enough, little Samuel looked up, and he heard the voice of divine Love calling: "Samuel! Samuel!"

And Samuel was so happy to know that it was divine Love calling him, so he answered and said what Eli had told him to say, "Speak, Lord, for Thy servant heareth."

Then divine Love told Samuel Love would always be with him, and Samuel was to serve Love all the time and show the people how to serve and obey Love.

Now, Eli had two boys, who used to help him in the Temple. But these boys listened to error, and this made them naughty. So error took these boys from the Temple of the Lord.

And divine Love put Samuel in their place, and because Eli did not teach his boys to love and serve the Truth, Love gave Samuel, when he grew up, charge over all the Temple of the Lord in the place of Eli. And everybody came to Samuel to learn more about how to love and obey God.

You may read about little Samuel in the book called I. Samuel in the Bible.

LITTLE DAVID

ONCE UPON A TIME, in the Bible days, there was a man named Jesse.

And Jesse lived in a town called Bethlehem, and Jesse had eight boys.

The name of the youngest boy was David.

David was the most beautiful boy you ever saw; he had rosy cheeks, bright eyes, and a lovely face.

David was a shepherd boy. Do you know what a shepherd is? A shepherd is one who takes care of the sheep and little lambs.

And his daddy, Jesse, had lots of sheep and lots of little lambs, and little David had to look after them and feed them, and watch that they did not get lost.

One day Love told Samuel to go to Bethlehem, where Jesse lived, and Love would show Samuel a little boy. And Love told Samuel some day when this little boy grew big enough, Love would make him king over the Children of Israel.

Samuel came to Jesse's house, and he talked with all of Jesse's boys, except David, for David was out in the big fields taking care of the sheep.

Jesse did not know what Samuel wanted with his boys, but he knew that Samuel always did what divine Love told him to do, so he told his boys to be very polite and obedient to Samuel.

Now, when Samuel had talked to all of the boys, except David, Love whispered to Samuel and said, None of these boys will I make a king. So Samuel said to Jesse, Haven't you another boy? Jesse said, I have a little boy, David, but he is out taking care of the sheep and the little lambs.

Samuel asked Jesse to send for David, so that he might talk with him, too.

So Jesse sent for David, and when David came Love whispered in Samuel's ear that David was the boy on whom Love was going to put a golden crown when he grew to be a big man, and make him a king.

Now David heard the voice of Love when Love whispered to Samuel, but David did not know what Love was saying. And from that day David loved the Truth and was obedient to Love.

So David went back to his sheep and little lambs, and he took good care of them for he would not let anything hurt the little lambs or the sheep.

One day a big bear, and a big, big lion came to David's flock of sheep (a flock means a lot of sheep together), and error made this big bear and big, big lion steal away one of the little lambs.

Do you know what David did? Why, he just walked right up to the big bear and the big lion, for David was not afraid at all because David knew that Love was right there with him, and Love would not let anything hurt him.

So David took the little lamb right out of the lion's mouth, and the lamb was not hurt at all.

Then Love gave David strength to separate error from God's animals, and take away all the power from error so error just became nothing. And David took the little lamb back to the mama sheep.

My, these sheep were glad to have little David bring back the dear, little lamb, and they all said, Baa! Baa!

Now little David loved to sing, so his daddy gave David a harp. Do you know what a harp is? A harp is a wooden thing, that has strings, and you pluck the strings and the sweetest music comes from it.

So David would sit by his sheep and little lambs, while they were eating the grass for their supper, and play on his harp and sing lovely songs and hymns. Oh! David was such a dear, sweet boy, and everybody loved him.

There was a king, who lived near where David lived, and his name was King Saul.

Now error was always whispering to King Saul, but King Saul did not really want to listen to these wrong thoughts.

So King Saul's servant told him he would get David to come to King Saul and play some lovely music on his harp. And then King Saul would not hear error at all. He would hear only David's beautiful music.

And when David came to King Saul, King Saul loved David and loved David's music, too. The sweet music made King Saul think about divine Love. You know when we are thinking of divine Love error becomes nothing. So David's music made King Saul very happy.

You will find this story about little David in the book called I. Samuel in the Bible.

DAVID AND THE BIG OLD GIANT

Now the error that was always whispering to King Saul began to grow bigger and bigger, until at last this error got so big it became a giant and called itself Goliath.

Do you know what a giant is? A giant is a big, tall man—a giant is as big as one daddy standing on the head of another daddy. That is just how tall and big this giant was.

Now Goliath the giant was the champion of an army of men called Philistines.

Well, Goliath sent word to King Saul that he was coming to take away King Saul's riches and hurt King Saul's soldiers, and would take all the soldiers away from King Saul.

Then error made King Saul so afraid of this giant error, called Goliath, that King Saul did not know what to do.

Even King Saul's soldiers were afraid of this giant error.

Then David left his sheep and little lambs, and came to King Saul, and told him that he was not afraid of this giant error, whose name was Goliath.

You see David knew that divine Love had all the

strength and all the power, and David knew that even though error called itself giant Goliath, it did not really have any strength or power to hurt God's perfect child.

So David asked King Saul to let him go to this giant and fight him, and thus save King Saul and the people from being afraid of Goliath.

But King Saul said, No, David could not go because he was afraid that Goliath would hurt David.

David said, Please, King Saul, let me go to this old error, the giant, for divine Love will take care of me; divine Love will not let error hurt me, and I will fight this error until it becomes nothing.

So King Saul told David he could go and fight Goliath, but told David he must put on King Saul's armour, so that if the giant struck David, the armour would keep David from getting hurt. An armour is a heavy steel suit, which soldiers wear to keep them from getting hurt.

Now David knew that he must not put his trust in any old steel armour to save him, for David knew that he must put his trust in divine Love to cover him all over with His loving arms and keep him safe.

So David told King Saul he would not need the steel armour, and David picked up five smooth stones out of the brook. You know, like the pretty stones you find along the beach when mama and daddy take you to the seashore.

Well, David put the five smooth stones in his shepherd's bag, and took a sling in his hand. A sling is made of a piece of leather, and you put a stone in it, and whirl it around, and whizz—it shoots the stone far away.

David looked up and there coming toward him was the old giant error, named Goliath. My, but that old error was angry, and came screaming at David to make David afraid of him.

But David was not one bit afraid. David knew that the five smooth stones which he had in his shepherd's bag were stones of Love. And David knew that the real name of this error was Hate, and David knew that Love always destroys Hate.

David said to the giant Hate, You come to me to hurt me, but I come to you in the name of "the Lord of hosts." (The Lord of hosts you know means divine Love.)

Then David took a stone of Love, and put it in the sling and whirled it around, and whizz the stone of Love went through the air and struck the giant error, and this giant error became nothing at all.

David had four more stones of Love, but he did not need to use them, because the first little stone had gotten rid of the giant error.

When the Philistines saw that the giant Hate (their champion Goliath) was destroyed by David's stone of love they ran away. And so David showed King Saul that there was no error for him to fear.

You will find the story about David and the giant in the book called I. Samuel, in the Bible.

SONGS TO GOD

Now you remember that divine Love told Samuel that He would make David king when he grew to be a big man.

So divine Love told the Children of Israel to put a golden crown on David's head and make him a king, because David had been so brave and good.

When David was made a king, the Children of Israel loved him because David loved God so much and also because David was good to everyone.

King David loved to sing hymns to God, to thank God, and also to let God know how much King David trusted God to do everything right for everybody.

So King David would often go off by himself to think about Truth and Love, and he would take his harp and play upon the harp such beautiful music.

Then King David would sing lovely hymns or psalms to God.

One day King David took his harp and went off by himself, where he could think about the time when he was only a little shepherd boy and took care of the sheep and little lambs.

Then King David thought about the way divine Love

takes care of His children. So King David thought to himself, why divine Love is the best shepherd in all the world, because divine Love takes the best care of everybody, and Love does not let them want for anything, but Love just gives them everything.

And King David thought to himself, just as I used to take the sheep to rest in the soft, green grass, where they could get the best grass to eat and lovely fresh water to drink; and just as I used to take the sheep in the right paths, even though the sheep had to go through paths where error seemed to be; and just as I would not let the sheep get scared because I would tell them I loved them and would look after them; just so does divine Love do the same for all of His dear children.

Then David picked up his harp and began to play and sing all these beautiful thoughts about divine Love being the true shepherd—and this hymn is called the Twenty-third Psalm.

You should ask your mama to read the Twenty-third Psalm to you. You will enjoy it so much, because it is beautiful.

There is another beautiful psalm or hymn in the Bible about Truth and Love which shows people not to be afraid, and this is called the Ninety-first Psalm.

You know sometimes error would just get way down in our secret thoughts, then we think that we are afraid. But if you ask your mother or your father to read this lovely Psalm to you, then these fear thoughts will vanish.

If only everybody would fill his secret thoughts with Truth and Love, instead of letting error hide in their secret thoughts, why, then everybody would be living in the secret place of the highest thinking, which, of course, would be thinking of Truth and Love all the time.

Divine Love spreads His love over everybody and covers up everybody so error cannot find them—just like a hen covers up her little chickens with her wings and feathers. And Truth stands in front of everybody so nothing can hurt them, and Love keeps them from being afraid of the darkness, and Love will not let any error come near anyone's home. And if error makes anyone fall, Love sends His angel to lift him up at once so he will not be hurt at all.

Even if lions and snakes would come, Love would not let them hurt His children, and Love gives His children eternal Life. Do you know what eternal means? It means no beginning and no end—not like a lead pencil with a point and an end—but just like the letter O which goes round and round, without a beginning or an end.

You should ask your mother to read the Ninety-first Psalm to you also, for it is just as beautiful as the Twenty-third Psalm.

You must learn to sing hymns of Truth and Love, like King David and Moses did, for they will make you happy as they did these two good men.

You will find these songs to God in the Bible in the book called Psalms.

WISE KING SOLOMON

King David had a little boy, named Solomon, and King David loved little Solomon very much.

So when little Solomon grew up to be a big man, his father, King David, put the golden crown on Solomon's head and made him king.

And David told the new King Solomon that he must always keep the Ten Commandments, and then Love would take care of him and Love would give him everything that was good.

Then King Solomon asked Love to make him wise, so he would know how to do everything the way Love wished him to do.

Then divine Love made King Solomon see that Love knew everything—that no one really knew anything at all, because Love knew it all—and divine Love made King Solomon see that King Solomon was the reflection of divine Love, and reflected all that Love knew.

Do you know what reflection means? You just look in your mama's mirror, and there you will see a little child who looks just like you. That is called a reflection.

Now that is the way divine Love made King Solomon wise, by making King Solomon see himself as Love's reflection, just as you see your reflection in your mama's mirror.

Now, one of the wisest things King Solomon did was to build a big church.

It was the first really big church built in the Bible days.

King Solomon remembered that his father David always wished to build a church for divine Love, but he was always too busy.

And when divine Love made King Solomon wise, King Solomon knew that no one should be too busy to work for divine Love.

We must always give to divine Love the first of all, then we help to make everybody happy.

And when we help build churches and Sunday schools we are giving first to divine Love.

Then Love brings all His children to these beautiful churches and lovely Sunday schools, where we can all pray and sing to Life, Truth and Love.

King Solomon called all the men to him to help him build this beautiful church for divine Love.

My! but King Solomon had these men make Love's church beautiful! I wish we could have seen it, for it was so very beautiful.

They built Love's church of the most beautiful stones, and King Solomon told the men to make flowers and trees out of gold and put them on the doors of the church. And they built lovely porches, and they called them King Solomon's porches.

And King Solomon put the two big stones, which had the Ten Commandments written on them, in a little ark, which looked like Noah's Ark. And King Solomon put the ark in Love's church where the Ten Commandments would be safe.

Then Love just filled the church with His presence and King Solomon told the Children of Israel that they must keep the Ten Commandments and be obedient children, and then they would never be afraid of sickness nor anything, for Love would take care of them and would not allow them to be harmed.

Then King Solomon gave the Children of Israel a big party, and they had so many good things to eat, and they

King Solomon dedicating Love's Church.

King Solomon put the Ark in Love's Church where the Ten Commandments would be safe.

were all so happy because they had all helped to build the beautiful church.

It took King Solomon and his men seven years to build the church for divine Love.

And don't you suppose they must have had a lovely Sunday school room in that beautiful church for the little children!

You may read about King Solomon and the beautiful church in the book called I. Kings, in the Bible.

ISAIAH TELLS ABOUT THE CHRIST CHILD

Once upon a time, in the Bible days, there lived a man named Isaiah, and Isaiah loved God and he talked with God and was obedient to God.

The Children of Israel were getting to be naughty, because they listened to error and they let it make them do naughty things until they forgot how to be good. And they thought being naughty was just the same as being good.

Then error tried to whisper to good Isaiah and tell him that the Children of Israel would never be good children again.

But Isaiah would not listen to error, for he knew that some day divine Love would send the little Christ child to the world to show the people how to be good again and follow divine Love. And the Christ child would also show them how to close error's mouth so it could not talk any more to them.

And this dear little Christ child would also make them see that they were all God's perfect children and were not naughty at all.

Then Isaiah told the Children of Israel that the little

Christ child, whom Love would send to them to teach them to see themselves as God's perfect children, would be the wisest and the most loving child there had ever been in the world.

This dear Christ child would not be afraid of anything and would teach the world not to be afraid even of animals, but would teach everybody to love all the animals so the animals could love everybody.

And Isaiah said when this loving Christ child would come, that the wolf and the little lamb and the leopard and the little kid would all lie down together; and the calf and the young lion, with all the other animals, would let this loving Christ child lead them.

And these animals would be just as tame and loving as could be.

Remember, children, to be always as loving to animals as the Christ child, then they will love you and never hurt you.

And Isaiah told the children of Israel when the Christ child came, that beautiful flowers would grow everywhere and everybody would be happy because the Christ child would make everybody well and strong, and would teach everybody how to keep well.

You will read about the coming of the Christ child in the book called Isaiah in the Bible.

The Christ-child would teach everybody to love all the animals so the animals could love everybody.

SHADRACH, MESHACH, AND ABED-NEGO

NOW, I AM GOING TO TELL you a story about three men who lived in the Bible days.

And these three men had the funniest names you ever heard. Their names were Shadrach, Meshach, and Abed-nego.

Shadrach, Meshach, and Abed-nego loved and obeyed God, and they were good and kind to everyone and kept the Ten Commandments all the time.

Now I am going to tell you another funny name, which belonged to a king who lived in the Bible days. This is a great long name, but I think you are big enough to say it, just as well as your big brothers and sisters say it. This is the king's name, Nebuchadnezzar. Did you ever hear of such a long, funny name?

Well, King Nebuchadnezzar listened to wrong thought which told him to break the First and Second Commandments, and he did break them.

For King Nebuchadnezzar made a big, graven image, or false god, of gold, and bowed down to it. And Nebuchadnezzar loved this graven image of gold, and called it a god, instead of loving the one God, who is divine Love.

Just think how foolish error made King Nebuchadnezzar behave to make a god of gold. You know if anyone had knocked this gold god over, it could not have even picked itself up, for of course it had no life in it.

King Nebuchadnezzar should have known that these wrong thoughts were just fooling him, and he should have known that God is Spirit and that gold can never be God.

But this error made King Nebuchadnezzar very naughty and told him to make all the Children of Israel bow down and kiss the false god made of gold.

But Shadrach, Meshach, and Abed-nego would not bow down nor kiss the false god made of gold. They had only one God, to whom to bow down and that was Spirit, Life, Truth and Love.

Then error made King Nebuchadnezzar get very angry with Shadrach, Meshach, and Abed-nego. And he called his servants to build a great big fire in a furnace.

Then King Nebuchadnezzar told his servants to tie Shadrach, Meshach, and Abed-nego's hands behind them, and to throw them into the big, fiery furnace.

So the servants tied Shadrach's, Meshach's, and Abed-nego's hands and threw them into the big, fiery furnace.

Now Shadrach, Meshach, and Abed-nego were not afraid at all when the servants threw them into the fiery furnace, because they knew that divine Love would stay with them and would not let that hot fire burn them.

And, sure enough, divine Love sent the Christ Truth to walk beside Shadrach, Meshach, and Abed-nego, and keep the fire from touching them.

Now, when King Nebuchadnezzar looked in the fiery furnace to see if Shadrach, Meshach, and Abed-nego were burned up, he called to the men who had thrown Shadrach, Meshach, and Abed-nego into the fiery furnace, and said to them, I thought we put only three men in the fiery furnace, but now I see four men walking in the midst of the fire, and the fire does not hurt them at all; and this fourth man who is walking in the fire with Shadrach, Meshach, and Abed-nego looks like the Son of God.

Then the king ordered his servants to take Shadrach, Meshach, and Abed-nego out of the fiery furnace, and they were not hurt at all, not even their clothes were burned.

Then the king made everybody bow down to and serve divine Love, instead of the false god he had made.

Because divine Love had kept the fire from burning Shadrach, Meshach, and Abed-nego, King Nebuchadnezzar knew that divine Love was the only God.

You may read this story of Shadrach, Meshach, and Abed-nego in the book called Daniel, in the Bible.

DANIEL NOT AFRAID OF LIONS

Once upon a time, in the Bible days, there lived a man named Daniel.

And ever since Daniel had been a little boy he had kept all the Ten Commandments; and he had been loving and kind to everyone. And Daniel had always been obedient to divine Love.

Now the king who lived in Daniel's time was named Darius, and Darius loved Daniel very much. And because Daniel was so wise and good and did everything just right, the king made Daniel a president, so Daniel could take care of the king's riches.

One day error whispered in the king's ear and told him to make everybody pray to the king instead of praying to divine Love.

If the king had loved God more he would not have listened to these wrong thoughts that told him to make everybody pray to him instead of praying to divine Love.

But you see, the king loved himself more than he loved God. That is why error came to King Darius to tempt him.

So the king sent word that for thirty days everybody should pray only to the king and ask him for all the things they wished to have, instead of praying to divine Love.

When Daniel heard this, he knew at once that error was talking to the king and that the king was letting error use his mouth to tell the people to stop praying to divine Love.

Do you think Daniel stopped praying to divine Love? No, Daniel was not afraid of error, and Daniel knew he must pray only to divine Love, for divine Love is the only God.

So Daniel went to his room three times each day and thanked divine Love for all of His goodness, and asked divine Love to make him more wise and loving so he could help everybody.

Now, when Daniel was praying to divine Love, his window was wide open and the king's princes went by and they heard Daniel praying to divine Love.

And error made the princes get very angry with Daniel for praying to divine Love instead of praying to the king, and the princes ran as fast as they could to tell the king.

And error made the princes say to the king that because Daniel had prayed to divine Love, they must throw him into a den where a lot of big lions lived so the lions could eat Daniel up.

When the princes told the king that he must let them throw Daniel to the lions, the king was so sorry he even let error use his mouth to tell the people they should not pray to divine Love. For King Darius really loved Daniel, and he did not want the lions to eat Daniel.

But the people did not care whether the king was sorry

for Daniel or not, error was going to make the princes throw Daniel into the den of lions.

Now the den where these big lions lived was made of big rocks, and it was very deep and dark down there, except on the top there was a hole through which a little bit of light came.

So these princes took Daniel and threw him into the den with all the big lions, and they put a stone over the top of the den.

Then the king went to his home and he could not sleep because he was so scared when he thought about Daniel in the den with the big lions.

Do you think Daniel was scared when the princes threw him into the den with these big lions?

No, indeed, Daniel was not scared one bit. Daniel knew divine Love had all the power, and divine Love would not let the lions hurt him for he was Love's obedient child.

When Daniel was first thrown into the den with the lions, Daniel looked up to find Love, and there, shining through the hole at the top of the den, was a beautiful Light, and in this Light, Daniel saw Love come to save him from the big lions.

So when these lions came toward Daniel error whispered that they should eat him up, but Daniel turned around and looked at the big lions without any fear, for Love was making Daniel's eyes see loving lions instead of lions made angry by error.

Then Love sent His angel to shut all the lions' mouths, and to take away all the error from the lions so they did not wish to hurt Daniel.

For Love was making Daniel's eyes see loving lions instead of lions made naughty by error.

And Daniel loved the lions and the lions loved Daniel, and they played together until the next morning.

Then wasn't the king surprised the next morning to find the lions had not hurt Daniel at all!

Daniel told the king the lions had not hurt him because Daniel had put all his trust in divine Love and divine Love had taken away Daniel's fear, and made him love the big lions, so the big lions loved him and did not hurt him.

The king was so happy and said from that time on he would serve divine Love, as Daniel did, and he would send word to all the people to pray only to divine Love, and to ask only divine Love for everything, as Daniel always did.

You may find this story about Daniel in the book called Daniel in the Bible.

THE STAR OF BETHLEHEM

Now, you remember that Isaiah told the Children of Israel that some day the Christ child would come and show them how to keep good and loving, and how they could stop wrong thought from coming to them to make them naughty.

Well, there were some men living in the Bible days who were so wise they were called the wise men.

And Truth told these wise men that the time had come when divine Love would send His Christ child to the world to bless everybody.

So these wise men got a bag and filled it with lovely gifts to give to the baby Christ when they found him.

Then these wise men got on their camels and took the gifts and rode away to hunt for the baby Christ.

Now the Christ means the Truth, so the Christ means the true child of God, or the perfect child.

That is why the wise men wished to find the Christ child, or the perfect child of God, so they could learn how to be perfect, too.

After the wise men had started off on their camels to find the baby Christ, they did not know which way to go. Then they looked up to the sky, which was quite dark, and, guess what they saw!

Why, they saw the most beautiful, twinkling star you ever saw. It was so big and full of light.

And this beautiful star is called the Star of Bethlehem.

So the wise men knew if they followed this beautiful Star of Bethlehem, which was twinkling so brightly in the sky, that it would lead them to the baby Christ.

So the wise men made the camels go faster and they followed the Star of Bethlehem.

Now there was a lady named Mary, who also was looking for the Christ child to come.

Divine Love had sent His angel to Mary to tell her He would send the Christ child to her to take care of until he grew up to be a man, for the Christ child would come first

Three Wise Men from the East bearing Gifts to the Christ Child.

as a little baby, and would need a mother to take care of him.

Now the day before the baby Christ came, and the day before the wise men saw the Star of Bethlehem, Mary went to the city called Bethlehem to stay all night. But that night all the rooms everywhere had been taken by other people, so Mary did not have a room to sleep in.

A very kind man told Mary he would let her sleep in the house where the camels and cows and sheep and lambs and chickens all slept. So Mary was glad to have a place where she could go to bed and sleep. And, besides, Mary loved all of Love's animals.

And early in the morning Love sent His angel with the baby Christ to Mary there in the stable with all the dear animals about. And Mary made a bed for the baby Christ in a manger. You know that a manger is a big box where they put the food to feed the animals.

Now the wise men kept following the Star of Bethlehem and at last the beautiful star led them right to the manger where the baby Christ lay fast asleep.

Then the wise men loved the beautiful baby Christ, and opened their bag and gave him all the gifts of gold and lovely perfumes, which they had brought him.

Then the wise men thanked divine Love for sending to the world the Christ child, and then they rode away on their camels.

Now, out in the field near Bethlehem, there were some shepherds taking care of their sheep.

And Love sent His angel to tell the shepherds the good news about Love bringing the baby Christ to Mary. And

Glory to God in the highest and on earth, Peace, Goodwill toward men.

the angel told the shepherds they would find the baby Christ lying in a manger.

Then, all of a sudden, the shepherds heard the most beautiful singing, and the shepherds listened because the singing made them feel so joyous and happy they also felt like singing to God for sending the baby Christ who would teach the world about divine Love being the mother and father of everybody.

Then the shepherds wondered where the singing was coming from, for they could not see anybody.

Then Love told the shepherds that it was His angels singing. And these are the words which the angels, called the heavenly host, were singing:

> *Glory to God in the highest and on earth peace, good will toward men.*

After the angels stopped singing, the shepherds went to the manger to see the baby Christ.

And, oh! how they did love the beautiful baby Christ. And the shepherds also thanked divine Love for sending the Christ child to help everybody.

Mary took the baby Christ back home, to Nazareth, to be his mother, and to take care of him until he grew up to be a big man.

And Love's angel told Mary to name the baby Jesus, so Mary named him Jesus as the angel told her to do.

You will find this story about the Star of Bethlehem and the baby Christ in two books in the Bible. One book is called Matthew and the other book is called Luke.

JESUS A LITTLE BOY

WHEN JESUS WAS A LITTLE BOY, he was the most loving little boy who ever lived.

Jesus knew divine Love was his only Father, and he knew whatever he did, it was his Father, divine Love, who showed him how to do it.

One day when Jesus was twelve years old, his mama, Mary, took him with her to a city called Jerusalem, where there was to be a big feast.

After the feast was over and Mary was ready to go home, she could not find Jesus anywhere. So Mary looked and looked, but still she could not find Jesus.

Mary hunted for Jesus three days, and then at last she found him.

Now, guess where he was! Jesus was still in Jerusalem; he was in the Temple, and some very wise and big men were talking to Jesus asking him a great many questions. The wise men did not know how to answer these questions themselves.

And Jesus answered all the questions and told the big, wise men things they did not know, but Jesus did know. Now, what do you think of that! A little boy knowing more than big men know!

How do you think Jesus happened to know all these big questions? Why, because Jesus' Father, divine Love, told Jesus the answer to every question in the world.

When his mama saw Jesus answering the questions of these wise men she was so surprised.

Then Mary asked Jesus why he had not come with her, instead of staying behind in Jerusalem.

So Jesus told her that he must be about his Father's business. And that business was to teach everybody about divine Love, and how to obey divine Love.

Then Jesus went back home to Nazareth with Mary, and he obeyed her always.

And Jesus learned to help Mary's husband to cut wooden sticks, and to build houses.

But Jesus also kept learning more and more about divine Love, and learning more and more of what his Father, divine Love, wanted him to do when he became a big man.

You may read this story about Jesus teaching the wise men in the book called Luke, in the Bible.

JESUS AND THE BEATITUDES

ONE DAY AFTER JESUS GREW up to be a big man, he was walking by the sea when he saw two brothers fishing. Jesus told these brothers, whose names were Simon Peter and Andrew, to follow him and he would teach them about Life, Truth and Love.

So Simon Peter and Andrew stopped fishing and followed Jesus.

As Jesus, Simon Peter, and Andrew walked along, Jesus saw two more brothers, named James and John, and they were mending their fishing nets. And Jesus called to James and John to join Simon Peter and Andrew, and follow him. And James and John stopped mending their nets and also followed Jesus.

Then eight more men came and followed Jesus.

That made twelve men who were following Jesus, and Jesus called these twelve men his disciples, and he loved his disciples very much.

One day Jesus went up into a high mountain to talk with his Father, divine Love.

And when Jesus was in the mountains, his disciples followed and climbed up the mountain to ask Jesus to tell them more about Life, Truth and Love.

Then Jesus showed them that they must climb up the mountain of Truth to be blessed or to be made happy.

And Jesus taught them nine footsteps, for them to take up the mountain of Truth, to receive Love's blessings.

And these nine blessings are called the Beatitudes. I will tell you some of the meanings that I have learned from the Beatitudes, and you may learn some other meanings also, for everybody learns more and more meanings as he studies these Beatitudes for himself.

This is the First Beatitude which Jesus taught his disciples:

> *Blessed are the poor in spirit: for theirs is the kingdom of heaven.*

When we see that we are not good ourselves, but that God is the only one who is really good, this is being poor in spirit. This makes us turn to God for all goodness. Then He gives us joy and happiness.

This is the Second Beatitude which Jesus taught his disciples:

> *Blessed are they that mourn: for they shall be comforted.*

When we feel sorry that we listened to error and we stop listening to error, Love blesses us by making us glad that we have turned away from error.

This is the Third Beatitude which Jesus taught his disciples:

> *Blessed are the meek: for they shall inherit the earth.*

When we are gentle, and listen to Love, Love will show us all the riches of truth which our Father-Mother-God has given to us.

This is the Fourth Beatitude which Jesus taught his disciples:

> *Blessed are they which do hunger and thirst after righteousness: for they shall be filled.*

When we wish to learn more of the truth, Love blesses us by teaching us more and more of the truth.

This is the Fifth Beatitude which Jesus taught his disciples:

> *Blessed are the merciful: for they shall obtain mercy.*

If we are kind to everyone, then we shall be blessed by having everyone kind to us.

This is the Sixth Beatitude which Jesus taught his disciples:

> *Blessed are the pure in heart: for they shall see God.*

If we have love in our thoughts all the time, we shall be blessed by seeing the good everywhere and in everybody.

This is the Seventh Beatitude which Jesus taught his disciples:

> *Blessed are the peacemakers: for they shall be called the children of God.*

When error seems to be making everyone angry and naughty, we must know that error is nothing.

And when we know that error is nothing, then peace is made at once and we are blessed by seeing Love everywhere.

This is the Eighth Beatitude which Jesus taught his disciples:

> *Blessed are they which are persecuted for righteousness' sake: for theirs is the kingdom of heaven.*

If error tells anyone to make us unhappy because we are following the Christ Truth, Love will bless us and make us happy because we are Love's obedient children.

This is the Ninth, and last, Beatitude which Jesus taught his disciples:

> *Blessed are ye, when men shall revile you, and persecute you, and shall say all manner of evil against you falsely, for my sake. Rejoice, and be exceeding glad: for great is your reward in heaven: for so persecuted they the prophets which were before you.*

If error makes anyone unkind to us, and mistreat us and tell naughty stories about us, because we are obedient to divine Love, we must not be afraid or unhappy, for error even tried to hurt Jesus. But it could not, because divine Love made error nothing. And so we must be glad that Truth blesses everyone.

You will find the Beatitudes, which Jesus taught his disciples, in the fifth chapter of Matthew, in the Bible.

JESUS MADE MANY PEOPLE WELL

WHEN JESUS CAME DOWN from the mountain where he had been teaching his disciples the Beatitudes, there was a big crowd of people waiting to see Jesus to ask him to make them well—because you see error had made them believe they were sick.

So Jesus told them they were God's perfect children and that God is Love, and Love made them perfect.

Then Jesus made error, called sickness, become nothing. And all those dear people were made well and strong.

Now there was a woman who followed Jesus, and error had made her believe that she had been sick for a long, long time.

And this woman thought, Oh! if only I can get near enough just to touch Jesus' clothes, I know that will make me well.

And when Jesus was out walking with his disciples, and a big crowd of people were following him, Jesus felt some one touch him. And Jesus said, Who touched me, but his disciples said, No one touched you, Master. (The disciples called Jesus Master all the time.)

Then Jesus turned around and saw the woman. And Jesus told the dear woman that because she believed divine Love would make her well, Love would make her well.

So Jesus made that error nothing, which had made the dear woman believe in sickness for so long a time. And the woman went home happy and well.

One day Jesus was in a house teaching a big crowd of people that they did not have to be sick, and that it was

Jesus told the dear woman that because she believed divine Love would make her well, Love would make her well.

only error which made them believe they were sick. And Jesus taught them that divine Love was their Father-Mother-God and loved them too much to ever let them get sick.

And a great many of the people, who were listening to Jesus making error nothing, were made well right on the spot.

Now there was a man who had been in bed for a long time because error had told this man he was sick and could not walk.

Just guess what they did with this man! Why, some of his friends took the bed on which the man was lying to the top of the house where Jesus was teaching and making the people well. And these men made a big hole in the top of the house, and lowered the bed and the man whom error made sick so he could not walk, down through the hole into the house, so Jesus could make him well as Jesus was making everybody else well.

Now the reason these men put the bed and the man down through the hole in the top of the house was because the house was so full of people, who had come to get Jesus to make them well, that they could not get another person in through the doors.

Wasn't that loving and kind of Jesus to make all those people well?

And as soon as Jesus saw the man, who was still lying on his bed, Jesus made the error nothing which was making the man stay in bed and was making him believe he could not walk.

And Jesus said to the man, "Take up thy bed, and go into thine own house."

Now, you see, Jesus had made error nothing, so there wasn't anything to hold the man to his bed any longer.

So the man got off the bed at once, for the man found he was perfectly well. And he obeyed Jesus and took his bed and went to his own home.

Jesus was taking a walk one day, and he saw a man. Error had closed the man's eyes tight so the man could not see, for he believed that he was blind.

So when Jesus passed by this man, whom error had made blind, the man called after Jesus, and asked him to open his eyes so he could see.

And Jesus told that error to get away from that man's eyes, for divine Love had made his eyes perfect. So Jesus made error nothing, and then the man opened his eyes and he could see everything.

How happy that man was that Jesus made him see. And so were all the people happy whom Jesus had made well and strong.

Jesus called his twelve disciples to him and taught them how to make error nothing so everybody in the world could be made well.

And the Christ Truth is teaching you and me and everyone, just as Jesus taught his disciples, to go everywhere and make error nothing, so everyone can be well and happy.

You may read about how Jesus made many people well in four books in the Bible; these books are called Matthew, Mark, Luke, and John.

JESUS BLESSED THE LITTLE CHILDREN

ONE DAY JESUS WAS VERY busy teaching the people about Life, Truth and Love, and he was also making them well.

Now, some mothers heard that Jesus was teaching these grown-up people all about Life, Truth and Love.

So these mothers brought their little children to Jesus to ask Jesus to bless their little children by telling them also about Life, Truth and Love.

But the disciples did not wish to let all the mothers bring the little children to Jesus, because they thought that Jesus had so much work to do that he would not bother with little children.

You see the disciples did not know how much Jesus loved little children.

When the disciples tried to keep the little children from going to Jesus, Jesus told them they must not stop little children from coming to him.

Then all these dear little children came running to Jesus, and he took them up in his arms and kissed them. And Jesus told the little children never to be afraid, for divine Love would always take care of them and let nothing hurt them.

Now when Jesus knew the Truth about divine Love taking care of little children, that was the way he prayed for them and blessed them.

One day the disciples asked Jesus which one of them was first with divine Love, and also which one did divine Love think was the greatest and the best.

So Jesus took a little child by the hand, and said to his disciples, A little child is first with divine Love.

Then Jesus told the disciples they must learn to be loving and obedient, just as God's perfect children are loving and obedient.

You may read this story about Jesus blessing little children in the books called Matthew, Mark, and Luke, in the Bible. These are the first three books of the New Testament.

Of such is the kingdom.

JESUS THE TRUE PEACE-MAKER

One day Jesus and his disciples got into a big ship to take a sail. And Jesus went to the back of the ship to take a nap.

Now while Jesus was asleep, error got into the ocean and made the waves angry and wild. Then error made the waves so big and high that they splashed right into the ship with the disciples, but the waves did not splash where Jesus was sleeping.

Then error made the disciples very scared, when they saw the big, angry waves coming into the ship.

So the disciples ran to Jesus and waked him up, and they said, "Master, save us."

Then Jesus said to the disciples, "Why are ye fearful, O ye of little faith?"

Jesus knew that the disciples should not have let their wrong thoughts make them afraid, but the disciples should have known divine Love would take care of them.

Jesus knew that divine Love is om-nipo-tent, and Jesus knew there was nothing of which to be afraid.

Do you know what om-nipo-tent means? It means all powerful and that is just what Jesus knew about divine Love, that He had all the power and nothing else had any power but divine Love. See if you can say om-nipo-tent. It is a big word, but I know you can say it.

Now when the disciples called to Jesus to save them, Jesus stood up and said to the angry waves, "Peace—Be still," and the error which was making these waves naughty and angry became nothing.

And the dear waves became so full of peace and quietness that they were just as still as could be.

Wasn't Jesus a wonderful peace-maker?

Not long after this, the disciples went out in the ship again. But Jesus did not go with his disciples this time on the ship, because he had gone up into a mountain to pray to divine Love.

So that night while the disciples were sitting on the ship, they saw Jesus walking on top of the water, just as you and I walk on the street.

Now, you know, no one had ever walked on the water before, and no one has ever, even to this day, walked on the water, but Jesus.

My, but the disciples were surprised when they saw Jesus walking on top of those big waves toward their ship.

But, you remember, I told you that Jesus knew that divine Love is om-nipo-tent, that is, He had all power to do everything.

And Jesus knew that divine Love was his Father, and that his Father, divine Love, gave Jesus the power to walk on the waves.

Now, when Simon Peter saw Jesus walking on the

water, he asked Jesus if Jesus would help him to walk on the water also, and Jesus told Simon Peter he would help him and told Simon Peter to walk toward him.

So Simon Peter jumped into the water, and started to walk to Jesus. Then error made the waves get big and angry to scare Simon Peter.

Now Simon Peter should have looked at Jesus all the time when he was trying to walk on the water, because Jesus, you know, was showing Simon Peter how to trust divine Love to keep Simon Peter on top of the water so that he would be able to walk on the water and not fall down under the waves.

But fearful thoughts made Simon Peter look at the waves instead of looking at Jesus. And Simon Peter listened to these thoughts which told him the waves were so big and jumpy that Simon Peter could not walk on them but would sink down under the water.

Then Simon Peter got very scared and he called to Jesus to save him from falling under the water.

Now you and I know that divine Love is under the water just as He is on top, for divine Love is everywhere. And Simon Peter should not have let error make him afraid when Love is everywhere taking care of His children.

Then Jesus took hold of Simon Peter's hand, and held him on top of the water, and told him not to be afraid, that divine Love would take care of him.

And Jesus asked Simon Peter why he listened to these wrong thoughts which told him he would fall under the water.

Then Jesus made the waves get quiet and peaceful, so they could sail back to land.

Jesus told all of his disciples to listen only to the voice of Truth, when they would never get scared.

And all the disciples loved Jesus more than ever, and they thanked divine Love for sending His dear son, Christ Jesus, to teach them how to be peace-makers like their dear master.

You will find the story about Jesus being a peace-maker in the books in the Bible named Matthew, Mark, and Luke.

TWO LITTLE FISHES AND FIVE LOAVES OF BREAD

ONE DAY JESUS AND HIS DISCIPLES got in a ship, and sailed away to a place where there were no houses and no stores—just a big open field called a desert.

Now, as soon as the people knew that Jesus had gone away into the desert, they all followed him. My, but there was just the biggest crowd of people you ever saw who followed Jesus. And they followed him into the desert, because they wanted Jesus to teach them about Divine Love, and also make them well.

So Jesus made them all well, and he told them about Life, Truth, and Love.

And the people were so happy and full of joy to be with Jesus and to be made well.

At last night came and these people were so far away from their homes they could not get back home in time for supper.

The disciples did not know what to do to feed them, because you know there were no stores in the desert, where they could buy food. So the disciples told the people that they had better go to the nearest town and buy their suppers.

But Jesus said, No, they do not have to go away to buy their suppers; we will feed them.

And Jesus told the big crowd of people to sit down on the green grass. Then Jesus told his disciples to bring him all the food that they had.

Then the disciples told Jesus, Why we have only two little fishes and five loaves of bread, which we bought from a little boy: that is all the food we have, and it is not enough to feed this big crowd of people. But Jesus told his disciples not to be afraid for divine Love would feed them all.

So Jesus took the five loaves of bread and broke them up into pieces, then he broke the two little fishes also into pieces.

Jesus thanked divine Love for the Truth, and then he gave the disciples the broken-up bread and fish to give to the people, who were sitting on the grass waiting to be fed.

The disciples thought that when they gave the bread and fish to only a few people, that there would be no more left for the rest of the people.

Now you just guess what happened.

You see Jesus knew that divine Love was everywhere and divine Love made everything, and divine Love could make hundreds of little fishes and hundreds of loaves of bread out there in the desert, just the same as He made the two little fishes and the five loaves of bread.

Now this is what happened. When the disciples passed around the two little fishes and the five loaves of bread, more fish and more bread kept coming—and still more fish and more bread would come. My, but the disciples were surprised to see the fish and the bread piling up in heaps and heaps.

But, of course, Jesus knew all along what would happen, because he knew that divine Love was piling up the fishes and bread so Jesus could feed the big crowd of people, who wanted to learn more about Life, Truth and Love.

At last, after the people had eaten all they could eat, guess how many baskets full of fish and bread were left over? There were twelve baskets left over!

And Jesus told his disciples to be careful and gather all the fish and bread left over and not to lose one piece of the precious food.

You may read this story about Jesus feeding the people with the two little fishes and the five loaves of bread in the four books in the Bible, called Matthew, Mark, Luke, and John. These four books are called the four gospels.

THE TEN VIRGINS

ONE DAY JESUS TOLD HIS DISCIPLES a little story about ten virgins.

He said that once upon a time there were ten virgins. A virgin means a young girl.

And five of these virgins were very wise and followed Truth, but the other five were very foolish because they let error fool them all the time.

Now these ten virgins wished to know more about Truth and Love, the true creator. So, one day, they were told that the bridegroom was coming that night to teach them about the true creator.

So the ten virgins took their lamps with them to the place where the bridegroom was coming, so they would have plenty of light to see the bridegroom when he came.

Now the five wise virgins, who really wished to follow Truth, took plenty of oil in their lamps, because they were wise virgins. But the five foolish virgins let error make them forget to take any oil for their lamps.

And the ten virgins waited and waited, and still the bridegroom did not come.

So when it got very late, and still the bridegroom did not come, the ten virgins all fell asleep. And as they were sleeping they heard someone call out, Here comes the bridegroom, wake up and go out and meet the bridegroom.

Now it had gotten quite dark, because you see it was very late in the night.

But the wise virgins did not mind it being dark because they had plenty of oil to burn in their lamps. And the wise virgins trimmed their lamps and their lights were bright and shining.

The foolish virgins, whom error had made forget to bring enough oil for their lamps, found that their lamps had gone out. So the foolish virgins asked the wise virgins to give them some oil right quick so they could see the bridegroom too.

Oh, no! said the five wise virgins, we just have enough for our own lamps, for we want our lights to be very bright when the bridegroom comes.

So the five foolish virgins went to the store to buy some oil for their lamps. And while the foolish virgins were gone, the bridegroom came.

And when the bridegroom saw that the five wise virgins had their lamps burning so brightly, he knew that they were ready to learn about Life, Truth and Love, who is the true creator.

While the bridegroom was teaching the wise virgins, the foolish virgins came back and wanted to learn also from the bridegroom, but he said, "Verily I say unto you, I know you not." He knew that they were not ready for this great truth until they had learned to be prepared to receive the bridegroom when he comes. So the door of understanding was shut to the five foolish virgins until they could learn to keep their lamps lighted, in order to see the bridegroom when he came.

You may read this story about the five foolish virgins and the five wise virgins in the book called Matthew in the Bible.

The wise virgins did not mind it being dark because they had plenty of oil to burn in their lamps.

THE GOOD SHEPHERD

ONE DAY JESUS CALLED HIS DISCIPLES to gather around him, and he told them that very soon he would leave them and go back to his Father, divine Love.

And Jesus told them that he would still be their good shepherd, and would watch over them, like other shepherds watch over their sheep; and when he would leave them, his Father, divine Love, would send His Truth to them to help them to follow in his footsteps.

Jesus told his disciples that he was the door of the Truth, for they could only get the Truth through him.

Then Jesus told them that after he was gone, error would try to get them to go through another door to try and find Truth.

But Jesus told them he was the only door, and they must not try to go through the door which error would show, for it would not be the door to Truth, but the door to error.

Jesus told them that as little sheep knew their good shepherd, so must they know Jesus to be their good shepherd and follow only him.

Then Jesus told his disciples that not only the disciples were his sheep, but that all the people in the world were his sheep, and he was their good shepherd and the door by which they could find the Truth.

And Jesus said, "My sheep hear my voice and follow me."

Aren't you glad we are all Jesus' sheep, and that he is our good shepherd to lead us to the door of Truth, Life and Love?

You will find about Jesus being a good shepherd in the book called John in the Bible.

THE LAST SUPPER AND THE LAST BREAKFAST

JESUS TOLD HIS DISCIPLES that he would leave them soon and go to his Father, divine Love.

And when they all came to the supper table, John sat next to Jesus, because he loved Jesus so much, and John leaned his head on Jesus' shoulder while Jesus told them all about his Father, divine Love.

And Jesus blessed his disciples and told them to follow Truth always, and Truth would lead them to where he would be with his Father, divine Love.

And Jesus told them he would prepare a place for them with his Father.

Then Jesus and his disciples sang a lovely hymn, and Jesus told them he would see them again very soon, before he went to live always with his Father, divine Love.

And then Jesus told them goodbye, and left them.

And one night, very soon after Jesus went away, the disciples were out fishing. And the disciples fished all night, and when morning came the disciples saw someone on the shore and they did not know who it was at first.

And Jesus called to them and asked them if they had caught any fish. The disciples still did not know it was

Jesus who was talking to them, so they said, No, we have not caught any fish.

Now Jesus knew the reason they had not caught any fish in their net was because they were not thinking Truth. Their thoughts were full of fear, and they were not believing in divine Love, as they should have believed.

So Jesus called to them again, and told them to cast their net on the right side of the ship and then they would catch heaps and heaps of fish.

Now Jesus meant also for them to cast their thoughts on the right side with Truth. Then Truth would fill their thoughts with so much love that everything good would come to them.

When Jesus told the disciples to cast their net on the right side of the ship, the disciples' thoughts at once became so full of Truth and Love. And then they cast their net on the right side of the ship, and oh, my! when they pulled in the net it was just filled with all kinds of fish, little fish and big fish.

Now as soon as John saw the heaps and heaps of fish, and found his thoughts so full of love, he knew at once that the man on the shore must be Jesus.

For John knew that Jesus alone would know how to make so many fish come to them at once.

John told Peter it was Jesus who was standing on the shore. Peter was so glad that he jumped into the water and swam to Jesus.

And when they came to the shore they saw bread and fish cooking on a big fire.

Jesus told them to bring the fish which they had caught.

Peter brought the net with the fish in it, and even though the net was full to the top with fish yet it did not break.

The disciples were so happy to be with Jesus again.

Then Jesus said, "Come and dine." So they sat down with joy to eat breakfast with their Lord and Master, Jesus the Christ.

And Jesus taught the disciples from the Bible, and he blessed them, and then Jesus left them and went to live always with his Father, divine Love.

You may read about Jesus' last supper with his disciples in the four gospels in the Bible—Matthew, Mark, Luke and John. The story of the last breakfast is told in the book of John.

PETER AND JOHN

ONE DAY PETER AND JOHN went to the Temple to pray.

There was a gate in front of the Temple, called the Beautiful Gate, and a man was sitting down by this gate and he could not walk, because error had told him he could not walk and the man believed this error. And error also told the man he did not have any money.

So when Peter and John came through the Beautiful Gate on their way to the Temple, this man asked Peter and John for some money.

Now Peter and John, when they looked at this man, knew the man really did not need the money as much as he needed to stop listening to these wrong thoughts which told him he could not walk.

And Peter and John knew that the Truth, which Jesus had taught them, would make this man walk.

So Peter said to the man, We haven't any silver or gold, but we have the truth, which is so much richer than silver or gold. And then Peter said, "In the name of Jesus Christ of Nazareth rise up and walk."

When Peter called upon the Truth, which Jesus had taught them to call upon, Peter knew that Truth would give strength to the man's legs, and make him walk. So Peter took the man by his right hand, and lifted him up.

You see Peter took hold of the man's right hand, to lift the man up, because Peter had called upon the right power which would lift him out of the wrong hand of error.

How happy the man was to get rid of error and to find out he could walk. And he just ran and jumped with joy, and he thanked divine Love for making him well, and he also thanked Peter and John for knowing the truth about him, which Peter and John had learned from Jesus, the Christ.

You may read this story in the book in the Bible called The Acts.

AN ANGEL UNLOCKED THE DOOR FOR PETER

PETER WENT MANY PLACES, making people well, as his master, Jesus, the Christ, had told him to do.

Then error made King Herod put Peter in prison. And when Peter was in prison, the other disciples asked divine Love to unlock the big, heavy doors of the prison and bring Peter back to them.

Now Peter was not one bit afraid locked up in this prison, for he knew that Love was right there with him. And Peter knew that Love would take him back to the other disciples.

And sure enough, one night while Peter was asleep, and King Herod had put two soldiers to watch so that Peter could not run away, guess what happened.

Why, divine Love sent His angel to the prison, and suddenly there came a great bright light in the prison which wakened Peter and the angel told Peter to come with him quickly.

When Peter jumped up to obey the angel, the heavy chains fell off Peter's hands. My, but Peter was glad to have error's chains fall off.

Then the angel said to Peter, Dress yourself and follow

me. And the angel went ahead of Peter, and all the heavy prison doors opened without any keys at all, because the angel told them to open.

You know there is no door shut to divine Love, but every door is opened for all of us by Love's angel whenever we follow Truth and Love.

So Peter was free again and he was so happy to go to the other disciples, and to tell them how divine Love had sent His angel and unlocked the door of the prison and set him free.

You may read this story of the angel unlocking the prison doors for Peter in the book in the Bible called The Acts.

PAUL AND SILAS SING TO GOD

Now Paul and Silas were new disciples of the Christ, for they learned to love Jesus from hearing Peter and John tell about their beloved master, Jesus, the Christ, who had gone to live with his Father, divine Love.

Both Paul and Silas wanted to follow the Christ, and they wanted to enter through the same door of Truth with Jesus' other disciples.

So Paul and Silas went about making people well, and teaching the Christ Truth, just like Peter and John did.

Then error told Paul and Silas to stop teaching the Christ Truth, but Paul and Silas would not stop serving divine Love, the one God.

So Paul and Silas were put in prison, just as was Peter when divine Love's angel unlocked the prison doors for him. And error tied Paul's and Silas' feet tight, so they could not walk while they were in prison.

One night, when it was very dark, Paul and Silas said their prayers and then began to sing to God, divine Love.

Paul and Silas knew that divine Love was right there with them, and this made them so happy, and that is why they were singing to God.

Then suddenly the old prison began to shake, and shake,

and shake. And Love opened all the doors which error had locked up tight. And Paul and Silas found that their feet were not tied any more, because Love had untied them.

Now when the watchman, whom error had put in the prison to watch so that Paul and Silas could not get away, saw the prison shake, and shake, and shake, and the doors all come unlocked, he asked Paul and Silas to save him from error. For the watchmen knew that when Paul and Silas sang to God, God opened the doors for them.

Paul and Silas told the watchman he must believe in the Christ, Truth, and then error could not hurt him.

So the watchman believed in the Christ, Truth, and Love took away all his fears and made error nothing so it could not hurt him.

Then the watchman took Paul and Silas to his house and gave them a fine dinner.

So they all sang to God together and were very happy.

You may read this story of Paul and Silas in the book in the Bible called The Acts.

LOVE LIFTED UP EUTYCHUS WHEN HE FELL

Now Paul was getting ready to sail away on a big ship, and all the disciples were together in a big room upstairs. And the room was just full of light, because Love was there.

And Paul was teaching the new disciples all about Life, Truth and Love. And he was telling them how to follow the Truth while he was away.

Now there was a young man, named Eutychus, who was sitting in a window, and he listened to error when error told him to go to sleep. And so Eutychus went fast asleep sitting up in the window.

Wasn't that a foolish thing to do? But then error only tells people to do foolish things, because, you know, error could not tell anyone to do good, because it is error.

Now error told Eutychus that he was sleepy and had to go to sleep, because error did not want Eutychus to listen to Paul telling about divine Love. For, you know, where divine Love is, error becomes nothing.

After Eutychus went to sleep, he did not know what he was doing, so he fell down, down, down, from the upstairs' window to the ground.

Now you remember that I told you this upstairs' room, where Paul was talking to the disciples, was full of light because Love was there.

So this light of Truth and Love, which was in the room, made the disciples know that God was Eutychus' life, and that error could not take his life away because God, divine Love, was right there giving him Life always.

Then Paul told the disciples not to be afraid, and for them to know that even though error had made Eutychus fall, Love would pick him right up.

So Love did pick Eutychus up, and he was not hurt at all. For Love made error nothing, so it could not make Eutychus fall any more.

You may read about Eutychus in the book in the Bible called The Acts.

PAUL NOT AFRAID OF SNAKES

Now when Paul was sailing in a big ship, error made a big storm come up and made the wind blow very hard.

Love told Paul the right way to sail the ship so the ship would not be hurt. So Paul went to the captain of the ship and told him that Love had shown him the way for the captain to sail the ship.

But the captain would not listen to Love's way, but he did listen to error's way.

And the first thing they knew, the ship had been torn to pieces, and they were all in the water. And the people who could not swim made little rafts of the boards of the ship and floated into shore on the rafts.

But Paul could swim, so he swam ashore. And when Paul got to the shore, he found some very kind people there, who built a big fire and dried his clothes and made him nice and warm.

Now you know, when there is a fire made of sticks of wood, you have to keep putting sticks on the fire to keep the fire burning, so Paul picked up more sticks and put them on the fire to make it burn up bright and crackling.

Then out of the fire jumped a viper, and the viper

fastened itself on Paul's hand. Do you know what a vi
is? It's a snake.

Everybody was scared when they saw the snake on Paul's hand, but Paul was not afraid at all.

Paul knew that the snake was error, and he knew also that error was nothing and could not harm God's perfect child.

So Paul just shook off this error, called a viper, and it became nothing.

And the people were not afraid any more, because Paul had shown them that divine Love was everywhere, even in the big fire.

You may read this story about Paul not being afraid of snakes in the book called The Acts in the Bible.

THE WHOLE ARMOUR OF GOD

NOW PAUL HAS WRITTEN A BOOK in the Bible called Ephesians.

And in this book Paul tells little children to obey their fathers and mothers, and if they are obedient, God will give them all the riches of Love to bless them.

And Paul also tells little children to put on the *whole* armour of God, so they can stand up, when error tries to talk to them, and not let error throw them down.

Now do you know what the whole armour of God is?

Well, I will tell you. An armour is something which covers you up so nothing can hurt you. So you see if you only put on half of the armour, then error could hurt that part of you which is uncovered; and so you see you must put on the *whole* armour, so error cannot reach any part of you.

Now God's armour is made of Truth, so you must cover yourselves with Truth and right thoughts and put the shoes of love and peace on your feet, and take the shield of faith so it will stop all the fiery darts of error. And you must put the helmet of Life, Truth and Love on your head, and take the sword of Spirit, which means the word of God.

Then keep knowing the Truth, that divine Love is om-nipo-tent. You have already met this word, om-nipo-tent, in the story about Jesus, the True Peace-maker, and you will remember it means all powerful.

Then you will have on the *whole* armour of God, which Paul tells you to put on so error cannot see you, feel you, nor touch you.

And Paul says, also, having done all by putting on the *whole* armour of God, we must stand in obedience, waiting, as a soldier waits, to get the command from divine Love.

THE LITTLE BOOK WHICH IS SWEET AS HONEY

NOW JOHN WAS THE MOST LOVING of all Jesus' disciples, and Jesus loved John very much because he was so loving.

And John said little children should love one another and if little children would be full of love, divine Love would be with them all the time and keep them from ever being afraid.

John said, "God is Love," and "perfect love casteth out fear."

John was so full of love himself and so pure, that he saw with Love's eyes, and heard with Love's ears, and he spoke with Love's mouth.

So when Jesus, the Christ, left the world and went back to live with divine Love,—and everybody was wondering how he could learn more about the Truth which Jesus had taught before he went away—John saw how divine Love would teach the people again how to learn more about the Truth, because, you remember, John was so pure and loving that he saw with Love's eyes, and heard with Love's ears, and spoke with Love's mouth.

And one day John saw an angel, who came from divine

The angel with the little book.

Love. This angel had a beautiful rainbow upon his head, and his face was so full of light that his face looked like the sun. And the angel set his right foot on the sea, and his left foot on the earth.

Now, guess what this angel had in his hand! Well, it was a Little Book, which the angel was holding in his hand, and the book was open. And John said to the angel, "Give me the Little Book."

Then the angel gave the Little Book to John, and told him that when anyone began to read this Little Book he would think the Little Book was so sweet that they would get a taste of sweetness like honey in their mouths.

But the angel also told John that after they had finished reading this Little Book, wrong thoughts would try to take away this sweet honey taste and make a horrid old bitter taste come instead.

And John looked and saw again with Love's eyes, and this time he saw a beautiful woman with the sun for her dress and she was standing on the moon, and there was a crown of twelve stars on her head.

And John saw divine Love give the Truth to this beautiful woman.

At first, the Truth which divine Love gave this beautiful woman was as small as the baby Christ, then it got as big as the Christ child, then it grew to be the perfect man of God.

Now you see this precious Little Book, which John saw, was to teach everybody more about the Truth, which divine Love gave to this beautiful angel to give to the world.

And John said, "I have no greater joy than to hear that my children walk in truth."

Now, when John said "my children," he meant you and me and everybody in the world.

So let us all walk in the path of Truth and Love, and learn all the Commandments and Beatitudes. Then we shall grow up big and strong and be happy and well.

You may read this story about the Little Book, which John saw and which the angel told him was as sweet as honey, in the book called Revelation in the Bible.

The stories on which the stories in this book are based, may be found in the Bible as follows:

Noah and the Ark: Genesis, Chapters 6, 7 and 8.
Obedient Abraham: Genesis, Chapter 22.
Jacob and Esau: Genesis, Chapter 25.
Esau Forgives Jacob: Genesis, Chapter 32.
The Little Boy Joseph: Genesis, Chapter 37.
Joseph a Big Man: Genesis, Chapters 42, 43, 44 and 45.
Moses and the Princess: Exodus, Chapter 2.
Moses and the Children of Israel: Exodus, Chapters 14, 16 and 17.
Moses and the Ten Commandments: Exodus, Chapter 20.
Aaron and the Golden Calf: Exodus, Chapter 32.
Little Samuel: 1. Samuel, Chapter 3.
Little David: 1. Samuel, Chapter 16.
David and the Big, Old Giant: 1. Samuel, Chapter 17.
Songs to God: 23rd and 1st Psalms: Book of Psalms.
Wise King Solomon: 1. Kings, Chapter 6.
Isaiah Tells About the Christ Child: Isaiah, Chapter 11, and other later chapters.
Shadrach, Meshach and Abed-nego: Daniel, Chapter 3.
Daniel Not Afraid of Lions: Daniel, Chapter 6.
The Star of Bethlehem: Matthew, Chapter 2 and Luke, Chapter 2.
Jesus a Little Boy: Luke, Chapter 2.
Jesus and the Beatitudes: Matthew, Chapter 5.
Jesus Made Many People Well: Matthew, Mark, Luke and John.

Jesus Blessed the Little Children: Matthew, Chapter 19; Mark, Chapter 10; Luke, Chapter 18.

Jesus, the True Peace-maker: Matthew, Chapter 8; Mark, Chapter 4; Luke, Chapter 8.

Two Little Fishes and Five Loaves of Bread: Matthew, Chapter 14; Mark, Chapter 6; Luke, Chapter 9; John, Chapter 6.

The Ten Virgins: Matthew, Chapter 25.

The Good Shepherd: John, Chapter 10.

The Last Supper and the Last Breakfast: Matthew, Chapter 26; Mark, Chapter 14; Luke, Chapter 22; John, Chapters 13 and 21.

Peter and John: The Acts, Chapter 3.

An Angel Unlocked the Door for Peter: The Acts, Chapter 12.

Paul and Silas Sing to God: The Acts, Chapter 16.

Love Lifted Up Eutychus When He Fell: The Acts, Chapter 20.

Paul Not Afraid of Snakes: The Acts, Chapter 28.

The Whole Armour of God: Ephesians, Chapter 6.

The Little Book Which is Sweet as Honey: Revelations, Chapter 10, and Chapter 12; 1. John, Chapter 4.